MORE SCHKOOL VERSE

Chosen by Jennifer and Graeme Curry

Illustrated by David English

Beaver Books

This anthology
is dedicated to DIGGORY, growing up
in his world of books

A Beaver Book
Published by Arrow Books Limited
62–5 Chandos Place, London WC2N 4NW

An imprint of Century Hutchinson Ltd

London Melbourne Auckland
Johannesburg and agencies throughout the world

First published 1986

Set in Linoterm Bembo by
JH Graphics Ltd, Reading

Made and printed in Great Britain
by Anchor Brendon Ltd
Tiptree, Essex

ISBN 0 09 942680 3

This book belongs to

....

Also available by Jennifer Curry

The Beaver Book of Skool Verse
Mary Had a Crocodile and other funny animal verse

With Graeme Curry
The Beaver Book of Revolting Rhymes
None But the Brave Poems of courage and daring

CONTENTS

GOING TO SCHOOL

Summer Goes

Summer goes, summer goes
Like the sand between my toes
When the waves go out.
That's how summer pulls away,
Leaves me standing here today,
Waiting for the school bus.

Summer brought, summer brought
All the frogs that I have caught,
Frogging at the pond,
Hot dogs, flowers, shells and rocks,
Postcards in my postcard box –
Places far away.

Summer took, Summer took
All the lessons in my book,
Blew them far away.
I forgot the things I knew –
Arithmetic and spelling too,
Never thought about them.

Summer's gone, summer's gone –
Fall and winter coming on,
Frosty in the morning.
Here's the school bus right on time.
I'm not really sad that I'm
Going back to school.

Russell Hoban

The Old School Bus

It takes twenty minutes from my house up the road
For the old school bus to deliver its load.
With its worn out engine and noisy brakes
That's the time it takes,
To talk about last night's telly,
Eat a fruit gum (without chewing),
Do your homework,
Write something rude on the steamed up window,
Or hide Tommy Meacham's satchel so as he won't
  find it
And be late again.

We all hate the bus, but it isn't to blame,
Because even without it we'd go to school just the
  same.
In fact we'd probably have to walk
And then how would we talk,
Or swop sandwiches,
Have bubble gum blowing competitions,
Sing dirty songs,
Or hide Tommy Meacham's satchel so as he won't
  find it
And be late again.

Although it's a curse and a bind and a blow
To wait for the bus in the rain and the snow,
It sometimes seems sad when we look at that bus
To think that one day it will leave without us.

Charles Davies

The Good, the Bored and the Ugly

A coachload of pupils
Get into their places –
The ones in the back seats
Make ugly grimaces.

The ones in the front seats
Are fairer of feature –
Directing the driver
And talking to Teacher.

The ones in the middle –
Halfway down the bus,
Just look bored and wonder,
'Oh, why all the fuss?'

Colin West

First Primrose

I saw it in the lane
One morning going to school
After a soaking night of rain,
the year's first primrose,
Lying there familiar and cool
In its private place
Where little else grows
Beneath dripping hedgerows,
Stalk still wet, face
Pale as Inca gold,
Spring glistening in every delicate fold.
I knelt down by the roadside there,
Caught the faint whiff of its shy scent
On the cold and public air,
Then got up and went
On my slow way,
Glad and grateful I'd seen
The first primrose that day,
Half yellow, half green.

Leonard Clark

The False Knight and The Wee Boy

'O whare are ye gaun?'
  Quo' the fause knicht upon the road:
'I'm gaun to the scule,'
  Quo' the wee boy, and still he stude.

'What is that upon your back?'
  Quo' the fause knicht upon the road:
'Atweel it is my bukes,'
  Quo' the wee boy, and still he stude.

'What's that ye've got in your arm?'
  Quo' the fause knicht upon the road:
'Atweel it is my peit,'
  Quo' the wee boy, and stil he stude.

'Wha's aucht thae sheep?'
  Quo' the fause knicht upon the road:
'They are mine and my mither's,'
  Quo' the wee boy, and still he stude.

'How mony o' them are mine?'
  Quo' the fause knicht upon the road:
'A' they that hae blue tails,'
  Quo' the wee boy, and still he stude.

'I wiss ye were on yon tree,'
  Quo' the fause knicht upon the road:
'And a gude ladder under me,'
  Quo' the wee boy, and still he stude.

'And the ladder for to break,'
  Quo' the fause knicht upon the road:
'And for you to fa' down,'
  Quo' the wee boy, and still he stude.

'I wiss ye were in yon sie,'
Quo' the fause knicht upon the road:
'And a gude bottom under me,'
Quo' the wee boy, and still he stude.

'And the bottom for to break,'
Quo' the fause knicht upon the road:
'And ye to be drowned,'
Quo' the wee boy, and still he stude.

Anon

It's School Today

I wake up early, it's school today,
I'll get up early and be on my way.
I wash my face, I brush my hair,
I hang my nightdress on the chair.

The breakfast table is all set,
I'll eat it quickly and feed my pet,
I wave to mum and shut the gate;
I'll have to hurry, it's half past eight.
The bus has gone. I'll run to school.
I pass the shops and the swimming pool.
I reach the gate: it's five past nine,
Goodness me! I'm just in time.

Anon

Red Cows

Red cows that line the dusty road,
Along my way to school;
There where the clustered gum-trees shed
A patch of shadowed cool.

You lift your slow, wise heads and stare,
Knee-deep among the grass.
I know you would not harm me; still,
I wish I need not pass.

As I trudge on, with whistled tune,
To keep my courage high,
Your slow, wise heads all gravely turn,
To watch me passing by.

Till, as I reach the bend, and see
The school-house, square and plain,
You drop your slow, wise heads to graze
The shadowed grass again.

Lydia Pender

The Wind

The wind was bringing me to school,
And that is the fast way to get to school.
So why don't you let the wind bring you
To school just like me? And you will be
In school on time, just like I was.

James Snyder (aged 6)

First Day at School

'I am not going!'
My mum grips my hand
Assuring that it's fun.
Suddenly!
Gates stare at me
That are bigger than my dad.
'Do they eat shredded wheat?'
They open
I walk in
Boys run about
Shouting.
A lady walks up.
'Whose mummy are you?' I say.
A bell rings.
Then a whistle blows.
Children walk in a big, big house.
Doors shut like prison gates.
My mummy's hand leaves mine
My last words are...
'Please look after teddy!'

Melanie Louise Skipper (aged 11)

Thinking

Sometimes I think teachers are fed up with me
because I keep forgetting what they say.
Often when they say things I am thinking
about something more important, like today

I am busy thinking out a patent bicycle
to pedal me uphill to school, and back,
with a top to keep the cold and wind and rain out,
a headlight and a proper luggage rack.

My feet and legs got wet again this morning,
my fingers have gone stiff and blueish-white,
my books fell in a filthy oily puddle.
I think I look and feel a proper sight.

'Think of Romans,' he keeps saying, 'racing
chariots...'
but I prefer to think of what it's like
in his nifty purple racer. He's forgotten
I race two miles uphill each day, on a bike.

Jane Whittle

SCHOOL THOUGHTS

School Buses

You'd think that by the end of June they'd take
themselves
Away, get out of sight – but no, they don't; they
Don't at all. You see them waiting through
July in clumps of sumac near the railroad, or
Behind a service station, watching, always
watching for a
Child who's let go of summer's hand and strayed. I
have
Seen them hunting on the roads of August – empty
buses
Scanning woods and ponds with rows of empty
eyes. This morning
I saw five of them, parked like a week of
Schooldays, smiling slow in orange paint and
Smirking with their mirrors in sun –
But summer isn't done! Not yet!

Russell Hoban

Impressions of a New Boy

This school is huge – I hate it!
Please take me home.
Steep stairs cut in stone,
Peeling ceiling far too high,
The Head said 'Wait' so I wait alone
Alone though Mum stands here, close by.

The voice is loud – I hate it!
Please take me home.

'Come. Sit. What is your name?'
Trembling lips. The words won't come.
The Head says 'Speak,' but my cheeks flame,
I hear him give a quiet sigh.

The room is full – I hate it
Please take me home.

A sea of faces stare at me,
My desk is much too small,
Its wooden ridge rubs my knee,
But Head said 'Sit' so though I'm tall
I know that I must try.

The yard is full – I hate it,
Please take me home.

Bodies jostle me away,
Pressing me against the wall.
Then one boy says, 'Want to play?'
The boy says, 'Catch' and throws a ball,
And playtime seems to fly.

This school is great – I love it.

Marian Collihole

First Day at School

My first day at school today.
Funny sort of day.
Didn't seem to learn much.
Seemed all we did was play.
Then teacher wrote some letters
On a board all painted black
And then we had a story and ...
I don't think I'll go back.

Rod Hull

This 'Ere School

This 'ere school is filthy,
This 'ere school is cold,
This 'ere school is full of rules –
Made for five year olds.

These 'ere teachers are boring,
I wonder if they're able –
To write non-stop an essay
Or to say by heart a fable?

This 'ere school's got children
Laughing by a wall
Maybe this 'ere school
Ain't so bad after all.

Stephanie Marshall (aged 14)

I Don't want to go to School Today

I don't want to go to school today,
'Cos I hate it,
'Cos it's Maths,
'Cos it's History,
'Cos it's being told off,
'Cos it's anything.

I *might* go to school today,
'Cos it's alright,
'Cos it's Woodwork,
'Cos it's Football,
'Cos it's Friday,
'Cos it's... OK.

I think I *will* go to school today,
'Cos there's chips,
'Cos there's films,
'Cos there's my mates,
'Cos she sits in the row in front,
'Cos she smiled at me.

Christopher Mann

The School

The houses are red and tall or small
With brown birds perched on the backyard wall.
The school where I work and play each day
Is made of stone and old and grey,
And rain can't wash away the soot
That covers it from head to foot.
It's full as a parcel of girls and boys,
Drawings, paintings, writing, toys,
Dinners, teachers, pets and noise.

Stanley Cook

Sounds of School

The footsteps of a running boy,
The rumble of traffic,
The deep voice of a teacher,
The babble of voices from another classroom,
The creak of a desk,
The click as a pen or pencil is put down on a desk,
The slither of paper, sliding across a desk,
The high-pitched sound of chalk being used on a
  blackboard.

Timothy Hearn

On a March Morning

A smell of warmth in the air,
A sea of books in the library,
The buzz of conversation,
Shouts of glee from a PE class,
The echo of feet running through the corridors,
The beginnings of bean plants,
A smell of burning,
Sleepy cars resting in the car park,
Tapping of the gardener's hammer,
Dewy grass scattered with daisies like snowflakes,
The remains of an orange scattered round a bin,
The beginnings of a currant pudding ...
Fish mobiles hanging from the ceiling,
Faces painted and stuck on the wall,

Mrs Newman is teaching English,
A sea with ships,
'Finishing off' time,
Mrs Sequeire teaching maths,
The beginning of an icy picture,
Mrs Saxon teaching reading,
Pictures of faces and monsters,
Miss Sumpster teaching writing,
Bird mobiles hanging from the ceiling,
Poetry and pictures,
Paper men and women hanging from the wall,
Mr Smith teaching geometry,
Drawing circles and shapes,
And a weasel and a stoat stuffed and on show.

Jacqueline Davis (aged 10)

Go Away and Shut Up

I asked my Dad why I had to be quiet
He said
  'Go away and shut up.'
I asked my Mum why I couldn't fly my
Kite she said
  'Go away and shut up.'
I asked my friend why I couldn't
Play with her she said
  'Go away and shut up.'
I knocked on the staffroom door and
Asked for Sir he said
  'Go away and shut up.'
I asked myself why everyone was
Saying
  'Go away and shut up.'
But no answer came all I heard
Was
  'GO AWAY AND SHUT UP.'

Colleen Boland (aged 10)

Oh bring back higher standards

Oh bring back higher standards –
the pencil and the cane –
if we want education then we must have some pain.
Oh, bring us back all the gone days
Yes, bring back all the past . . .
let's put them all in rows again – so we can see who's
  last.

Let's label all the good ones
(the ones like you and me)
and make them into prefects – like prefects used to
be.
We'll put them on the honours board
. . . as honours ought to be,
and write their names in burnished script –
for all the world to see.
We'll have them back in uniform,
we'll have them doff their caps,
and learn what manners really are
. . . for decent kind of chaps!
. . . So let's label all the good ones,
we'll call them 'A's and 'B's –
and we'll parcel up the useless ones
and call them 'C's and 'D's.
. . . We'll even have an 'E' lot!
. . . an 'F' or 'G' maybe!!
. . . so they can know they're useless,
. . . and not as good as me.

For we've go to have the stupid –
And we've got to have the poor
Because –
    if we don't have them . . .
    well . . . what are prefects for?

Peter Dixon

The Magician

From my classroom window I can see a scrap-yard
where the cars are piled on top of each other
like souls in purgatory,
they are the dis-assembling dreams of panel-beaters.
Only a broken fence and a gate hanging
on the gibbet of a single hinge
separate them from their landscape
of broken, churned-up grass
where gipsies' horses and iron wheels
walked yesterday.
Then there are the shacks where the dogs are
tethered,
barking and crazy all day,
and an enclosure for hens
where the birds run senseless in the pelting rain,
and skirting it all
the dull backs of terraced houses
with their broken chimney cowls and bins,
and the rain, the incessant rain, beating like a
timpany
on the roofs of the cars and splashing like
acupuncture
in the puddled field.

And there is a man's pigeon loft:
I think he is a magician,
for every morning as he walks on this sea of
wreckage,
the rain stops, the grass seems to stiffen, the roof-
tops glisten,
and even the cars take on that frozen intensity
of still life after rain.
The man lifts his arm,
the sun rises,
the loft door opens
and a hundred swirling, tumbling acrobats cascade
and dance
in the dismal air.
And other birds squawk and cry and reel, magpies,
pee-wits,
seagulls, far from the coast, attracted by the water,
climb
and build around the column of the sun.

The man lowers his arm
and bows to me.
The children stare at him –
they can see that he has changed a landscape
which their teacher thought was ugly
into the trappings of music, and the movement of
wings.

Shaun Traynor

I Don't Know

I am sitting here, trying to think,
Trying to think of a poem.
Mr Bell says to me 'What are you going to write
about?'
I don't know.

I am sitting here trying to think,
Trying to think of a poem.
My friends have done a page but I've done nothing.
I don't know.

I am sitting here, trying to think,
Trying to think of a poem.
Mr Bell says 'I will be very angry if you haven't
done anything.'
I don't know.

I am sitting here, trying to think,
Trying to think of a poem.
Mr Bell's coming round. 'That's good,' says Mr
Bell.
I looked at the page and it was full of a poem called –
I Don't Know.

Mhairi Boyle (age 10)

Red Ink

The day I borrowed Miss Ward's red ink,
I'd nearly opened it and she gave me a wink.
'Don't open it,' she said to me,
I wondered why, so I thought I'd see.
I opened the bottle as slowly as I could,
I was nearly there, and I wondered if I should.
I was so curious of what was inside,
When I opened it I nearly died.
Oh why Miss Ward did you give me a wink?
Because in the bottle was. . . normal red ink.

Sarah Rogers (age 10)

The Computer
(A Pantoum)

A Pantoum is a verse form from south-east Asia.

We've got a computer at school,
we use it when teachers are out,
we know it's A TECHNICAL TOOL
which is what OUR GREAT FUTURE's about.

We use it when teachers are out
to PLAY all THE GAMES we enjoy
which is what OUR GREAT FUTURE's about.
We will need every NEW KIND OF TOY.

To PLAY all THE GAMES we enjoy
when we leave school to LEAD OUR OWN LIVES
we will need every NEW KIND OF TOY.
THE ONE WHO LEARNS FASTEST SURVIVES.

When we leave school to LEAD OUR OWN LIVES
computers will CUT DOWN THE LABOUR.
THE ONE WHO LEARNS FASTEST SURVIVES
to look after THE BEGGAR MY NEIGHBOUR.

Computers will CUT DOWN THE LABOUR,
THE PEOPLE who use them WILL RULE
to look after THE BEGGAR MY NEIGHBOUR.
We've got a computer at school.

Jane Whittle

SCHOOL PUPILS

Ten Little Schoolboys

Ten little schoolboys went out to dine;
One choked his little self, and then there were nine.

Nine little schoolboys sat up very late;
One overslept himself, and then there were eight.

Eight little schoolboys travelling to Devon;
One said he'd stay there, and then there were seven.

Seven little schoolboys chopping up sticks;
One chopped himself in half and then there were
six.

Six little schoolboys playing with a hive;
A bumble bee stung one, and then there were five.

Five little schoolboys going in for law;
One got in chancery, and then there were four.

Four little schoolboys going out to sea,
A red herring swallowed one, and then there were
three.

Three little schoolboys walking in the zoo;
A big bear hugged one, and then there were two.

Two little schoolboys sitting in the sun;
One got frizzled up, and then there was one.

One little schoolboy living all alone;
He got married, and then there was none.

Anon

Johnson Broke my Ruler, Sir

Johnson broke my ruler, sir,
He did, sir, honest;
Johnson broke my ruler, sir;
Please sir, that's not fair!

Johnson did it *twice,* sir;
He did, sir, honest:
Johnson did it *twice,* sir,
Please sir, he *did*!

Can't you make him stop it, sir?
Please sir, please?
Can't you make him stop it, sir?
I didn't do a thing!

Why's it me that's punished, sir?
Why, sir, why?
Why's it me that's punished, sir?
I only got him back.

Please don't tell my Dad, sir;
Please don't, please;
Please don't tell my Dad, sir;.
I won't do that again.

Johnson had it coming, sir;
Please sir, he did.
Johnson had it coming, sir;
(Stupid little kid).

Christopher Mann

The Fight

I remember, when we were just nippers,
Michael Saunders and I were sworn foes;
One morning of sunlit September
It looked as though we'd come to blows.

At playtime, quite close to the railings,
Out of sight from our teacher, Miss Bee,
I threatened that awful boy, Saunders,
And he in his turn threatened me.

He said that he'd tear me to ribbons.
'You and whose army?' I said.
(We were terribly witty in those days.)
I told him I'd kick in his head.

We circled each other like panthers
(Out of range of each other, of course);
We glared at each other like tigers,
Observed by the greengrocer's horse.

A little crowd gathered around us;
They egged us both on to begin.
Kathy Woodward (who wetted her knickers)
Said she'd notify our next-of-kin.

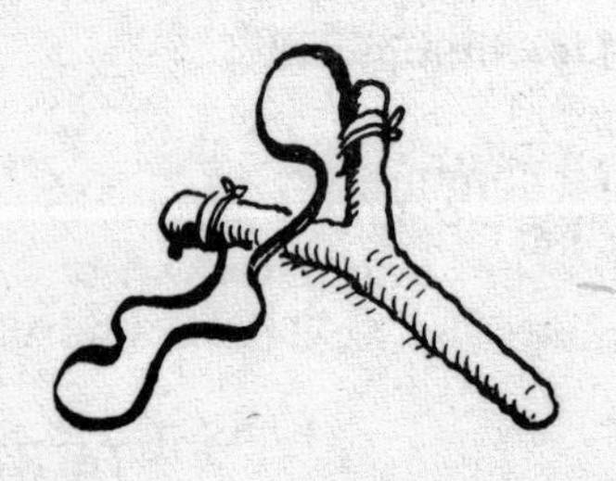

Someone pushed me towards Michael Saunders;
Thank God, he stepped out of the way.
We started to take off our jackets . . .
A Spitfire, it was, saved the day.

Overhead, the Battle of Britain
Was beginning in earnest once more;
Like tigers and panthers, the aircraft
Were trying to settle the score.

They spat at each other with bullets;
When two of them fell in their flames
Miss Bee led us all to the shelters
To play mental arithmetic games.

Sometimes I see Michael Saunders
In the pub of a Saturday night.
Forty years have elapsed since that morning
When two little boys had a fight:

But Michael still often reminds me
Of that day. What he always says is:
'I bet you my Dad could beat your Dad.'
And I tell him that mine could beat his.

We play cards in the cosy bar-parlour,
Our glasses of beer side by side;
In the grate a brisk log-fire is burning;
We forget that it's winter outside

Where, in the adjacent graveyard,
Two pilots lie under the snow.
I wonder if Michael or I might have won:
But that's something that we'll never know.

Ted Walker

The Rebel Child

Most days when I
Go off to school
I'm perfectly contented
To follow the rule,

Enjoy my history,
My music, my sums,
Feel a little sorry
When home time comes.

But on blowabout mornings
When clouds are wild
And the weather in a tumult –
I'm a rebel child.

I sit quite calmly,
My face at rest,
Seem quite peaceable,
Behave my best;

But deep inside me
I'm wild as a cloud,
Glad the sky is thrown about
Glad the storm's loud!

And when school's over
And I'm out at last,
I'll laugh in the rain,
Hold my face to the blast,

Be free as the weather,
Bellow and shout,
As I run through all the puddles –
'School's out! School's out!'

Leslie Norris

Playing Truant

Davy
was no fan
of the School Attendance man

Maybe
canes and schools
aren't really suitable for fools

the Law
still demanded
that school should be attended

what's more
the Headmaster
proclaimed him a disaster

being no
great bookworm
his liking for lessons was lukewarm

even so he was fluent
in the art of playing truant

Raymond Wilson

The Leader

I wanna be the leader
I wanna be the leader
Can I be the leader?
Can I? I can?
Promise? Promise?
Yippee, I'm the leader
I'm the leader

OK what shall we do?

Roger McGough

When I was lonely

Once we were all friends,
But day after day they left people out.
Monday it was me,
Nobody to play with,
Stamping my feet on the floor,
Kicking the stones about the playground,
Standing against the wall,
Sitting on my own at dinner time,
Surrounded by boys.
Bell goes, nobody to walk home with,
My head sinks to my chest.
The journey home seemed a long way.
Today.

Teresa Steele (aged 11)

The Loner

He leans against the playground wall,
Smacks his hands against the bricks
And other boredom-beating tricks,
Traces patterns with his feet,
Scuffs to make the tarmac squeak,
Back against the wall he stays –
And never plays.

The playground's quick with life,
The beat is strong.
Though sharp as a knife
Strife doesn't last long.
There is shouting, laughter, song,
And a place at the wall
For who won't belong.

We pass him running, skipping, walking,
In slow huddled groups, low talking.
Each in our familiar clique
We pass him by and never speak,
His loneness is his shell and shield
And neither he nor we will yield.

He wasn't there at the wall today,
Someone said he'd moved away
To another school and place
And on the wall where he used to lean
Someone had chalked
'watch this space'.

Julie Holder

Us Dreads

In a dis ya skool
us dreads rool.
Soul head dem saaf
mek us dreads laugh
dem no no how fe dress
but us dreads strickly de bess.
Gal dem cool an
control dem part ah de skool.
Mek us dreads feel sweet
each day ah de week.
Teachars all weird
mek saaf buoy scared
but us dread move together
an control de skool.
De music we play
nice up de day.
Rythdym just nice it
Teachar dem no like it.
When exam come
some dreads run
dem carn do dem tings.
In de enn teachar dem win.
Us dreads carn get na wok
we strickly brok
lose out in de enn
but us dreads still frienn.

Dave Martin

I am a Deemmun

Im a deemmun
I dont no how to spel
I allwaze deay-dreem
and teechuz pik on mi
cos I dont kno how to reed
I dont kair wot pepel sai
I dont nead to reed or ryte
I am not goeng to chooz it in the
therd yeers an
I dont nede it in my Jobb –
Soh thair!
Whot do I kare!

Julia Ignatiou

The Bully

'Where do you live?' the bully said.
'I'll not tell you,' said I.
'Tell me or I'll bash you up,'
But I did not reply.
He advanced on me, his fist upraised;
I stood firmly on my feet.
Then he punched me on the nose
So I said, '23 Albert Street.'

Rod Hull

Thug

School began it.
There he felt
the tongue's salt lash
raising its welt

on a child's heart.
Ten years ruled
by violence left him
thoroughly schooled,

nor did he fail
to understand
the blow of the
headmaster's hand.

That hand his hand
round the cosh curled.
What rules the classroom
rocks the world.

Raymond Garlick

The Bully

There is a boy in our class,
Who makes me blooming sick,
If I thought he wouldn't belt me,
I'd tell him he was thick.

He thinks he's very clever,
Always looking for a fight,
One of these days I'll bash him,
Then run away in fright.

When I grow one inch taller,
I'll hit him on the nose,
That is unless he acts quite smart,
And stands up on his toes.

I hate his ugly face,
I hate the little blighter,
I'd hit him in his weak spot,
If I was a better fighter.

Paul Dingle

Dumb Insolence

I'm big for ten years old
Maybe that's why they get at me

Teachers, parents, cops
Always getting at me

When they get at me

I don't hit em
They can do you for that

I don't swear at em
They can do you for that

I stick my hands in my pockets
And stare at them

And while I stare at them
I think about sick

They call it dumb insolence

They don't like it
But they can't do you for it

I've been done before
They say if I get done again

They'll put me in a home
So I do dumb insolence

Adrian Mitchell

That's Me

Everything that happened that morning is so clear
  to me,
Although it was all three months ago.
'Will you be all right, mum – you don't seem well?'
'Yes, off to school like a good girl.'
But I don't understand decimals this morning.
I don't want to change my library book,
  and yet I love reading.
Must I go to the swimming-baths this afternoon?
Although I know I'm nearly ready for my green
  braid.
  I want to go *home.*
The four o'clock bell,
I race up the road until my breath heaves in my
  throat.
Near home I dawdle, linger, drag –
I can hear my own heart
  and my own footsteps.
A rush of speed up the path –
  a dash at the door –
Dad's smiling face meets me,
His laughing voice tells me I have a new brother.
'You're the eldest, you choose his name.'

The eldest! the big sister!
  That's ME.

Julie Andrews

A Stomach-ache is Worse Away from Home

'Sir,' I said,
Hoping for sympathy,
'I've got the stomach-ache.'
All of it was true,
There was no putting it on.
I gave out winces with my mouth
Using my eyebrows skilfully
And held the hurt place hard
With both hands.
But it was my white face convinced him.
So he sent me outside
To walk it away in the fresh air.
Outside it was deathly cold.
Because he had his hand up first
Trev came out too
To see I was all right.
A grey wind with rain in it
Whipped across the playground,
Spattering through puddles
And setting the empties rolling
Up and down, up and down
And clatter-rattling in their crates.
Trev said, 'You'll be alright.'
And started kicking a tennis ball
Up against the toilet wall,
His hands in his pockets,
Bent against the cold.

The dinner ladies came out.
Moaning slightly I bent over
And gritted my teeth bravely.
But they didn't see
And walked through the school gates laughing.
At home there would be the smell of cooking
And our Robbo asleep before the fire.
I looked through the railings
And thought my way to our house.
Past the crumbling wall,
The Bingo Hall,
The scraggy tree
As thin as me,
The rotting boarding
By the cinema
With last week's star
In a Yankee car
Flapping on the hoarding.
Stop!
Turn right towards town
And three doors down,
That's our house.

Gareth Owen

The Lesson

'Your father's gone,' my bald headmaster said.
His shiny dome and brown tobacco jar
Splintered at once in tears. It wasn't grief.
I cried for knowledge which was bitterer
Than any grief. For there and then I knew
That grief has uses – that a father dead
Could bind a bully's fist a week or two;
And then I cried for shame, then for relief.

I was a month past ten when I learnt this:
I still remember how the noise was stilled
In school-assembly when my grief came in.
Some goldfish in a bowl quietly sculled
Around their shining prison on its shelf.
They were indifferent. All the other eyes
Were turned towards me. Somewhere in myself
Pride, like a goldfish, flashed a sudden fin.

Edward Lucie-Smith

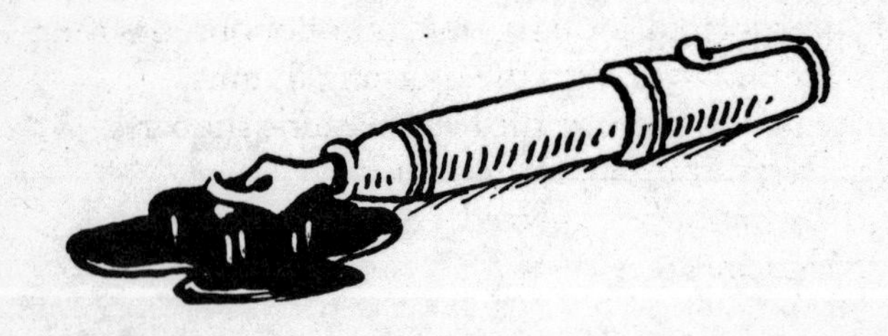

Schoolboy

Oh yes, I remember him well, the boy you are
searching for;
he looked like most boys, no better, brighter, or
more respectful;
he cribbed, mitched, spilt ink, rattled his desk and
garbled his lessons, with the worst of them;
he could smudge, hedge, smirk, wriggle, wince,
whimper, blarney, badger, blush, deceive, be
devious, stammer, improvise, assume
offended dignity or righteous indignation as though
to the manner born;
sullenly and reluctantly he drilled, for some small
crime, under Sergeant Bird, so wittily nicknamed
Oiseau, on Wednesday half-holidays,
appeared regularly in detention classes,
hid in the cloakroom during algebra,
was, when a newcomer, thrown into the bushes of
the
Lower Playground by bigger boys,
and threw newcomers into the bushes of the Lower
Playground when he was a bigger boy;
he scuffled at prayers,
he interpolated, smugly, the time-honoured wrong
irreverent words into the morning hymns,
he helped to damage the headmaster's rhubarb,
was thirty-third in trigonometry,
and, as might be expected, edited the School
Magazine.

Dylan Thomas

The Bionic Boy

It really fills me full of joy
To be the first bionic boy;
To know that I have got the power
To run at sixty miles an hour,
To punch my way through doors and walls,
To juggle with three cannon-balls,
To rope a steer or buffalo,
To tie a steel rod in a bow,
To uproot trees, break out of jails,
To fight successfully with whales,
To stop the traffic in the Strand
By waving my bionic hand,
To swim to Cap Gris-Nez and back
And then lay low the whole Welsh pack.
There's just one thing I must explain,
I haven't a bionic brain;
A matter of profound regret,
For I've no 'O'-levels as yet.

Charles Connell

Tom's Bomb

There was a boy whose name was Tom,
Who made a high explosive bomb,
By mixing up some iodine
With sugar, flour and plasticine.
Then, to make it smell more queer,
He added Daddy's home-made beer.
He took it off to school one day,
And when they all went out to play,
He left it by the radiator.

As the heat was getting greater,
The mixture in the bomb grew thick
And very soon it seemed to tick.
Miss Knight came in and gazed with awe
To see the bomb upon the floor.
'Dear me,' she said, 'it is a bomb,
An object worth escaping from.'
She went to Mr. Holliday
And said in tones that were not gay,
'Headmaster, this is not much fun;
There is a bomb in Classroom One.'
'Great snakes,' said he, and gave a cough
And said, 'I hope it won't go off.
But on the off-chance that it does,
I think we'd better call the fuzz.'
A policeman came and said, 'Oh God,
We need the bomb disposal squad,
Some firemen and a doctor too,
A helicopter and its crew,
And, since I'm shaking in the legs,
A pot of tea and hard-boiled eggs.'
A bomb disposal engineer
Said, with every sign of fear,
'I've not seen one like that before,'
And rushed out, screaming, through the door.
Everyone became more worried
Till Tom, who seemed to be unflurried,
Asked what was all the fuss about?
'I'll pick it up and take it out.'
He tipped the contents down the drain
And peace and quiet reigned again.
Tom just smiled and shook his head
And quietly to himself he said:
'Excitement's what these people seek.
I'll bring another one next week.'

David Hornsby

Government Health Warning

The boy stood on the burning desk,
Whence all but he had fled,
He tried to quench the flames with ink
(Which happened to be red);

The fire brigade came rushing round,
With ladders, hose and men:
They tried to reach the stricken lad
But flames roared up again.

'Oh help me, please, Oh help me!
He cried in grief and pain;
'Just get me out; I promise you
I'll never smoke again!'

The firemen they came running
And grabbed the little fool:
And soon he stood there safe and sound
Outside the blazing school.

His friends all gathered round and said:
'Thank God you're in one piece!
We thought they'd never get you out!
Will wonders never cease?'

But then a look of horror ran
Across the young lad's brow;
'I've left a pack of Marlboros there
I don't half need one now!'

Before the watchers scarce could move
Or even cry in fright;
He dashed into the flames again,
And vanished from their sight.

The flames leapt up, and caught the roof,
And down in dust it fell:
And never did they see again
The boy whose tale I tell.

So heed my words, and listen well
If you would live in wealth:
For smoking isn't just a joke.
It *damages* your health!

Christopher Mann

Lizzie

When we went over the park
Sunday mornings
We picked up sides

Lizzie was our centre-forward
Because she had the best shot.

When the teachers
Chose the school team
Marshie was our centre-forward.

Lizzie wasn't allowed to play,
They said.

So she watched us lose, instead.

Michael Rosen

Big Jim

When we play cricket, we don't let Jim bowl;
And when we play baseball, we don't let Jim bat.
But when we play football, we put Jim in goal,
For balls can't get past him, because Jim's so fat.

Colin West

The Changeling

Mary's mother is tall and fair,
Her father is freckled with ginger hair,
And they live in a house all polished and neat
In the very centre of Riverside Street.

But Mary is dark and thin and wild,
And she doesn't laugh like a human child,
And she doesn't cry like you and me
With tears as salt as the brooding sea.

For when Mary giggles the rattling sound
Is worse than the traffic for miles around;
And the sobs that heave Mary's shoulders high,
Leave her throat parched and her wide eyes dry.

In the classroom Mary works on her own,
And she plays in the playground quite alone.
In church she will not pray or sing,
For she never will join in anything.

It can only be that ten years ago,
In hurtling sleet and blinding snow,
Some dreaming wizards or spiteful elves
Went cradle-swapping to please themselves,

Took the real Mary to join their race
And left their fledgeling, in her place,
To grow both beautiful and sly
With power to destroy in her evil eye.

And the only thing both Marys share
Is that they are homesick everywhere.
So sumptuously by the fairies fed,
The one is hungry for human bread.

The other however the heat's turned higher
Is cold for the lack of fairy fire.
And the parents cannot know what is meant
By their daughter's waspish discontent.

Her sulks and tempers are never done,
She's a stock of harsh words for everyone;
While they, dismayed by their puzzling fate,
Go to bed early and get up late.

So now the mother is bent and grey,
And the father sits in his chair all day,
And Riverside Street cannot abide
The slum that their house has become inside.

Shirley Toulson

LESSONS

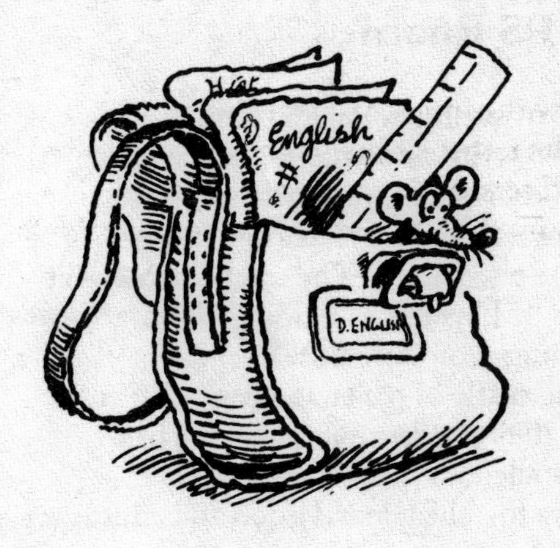

Riddle

I have no voice and yet I speak to you,
I tell of all things in the world that people do;
I have leaves, but I am not a tree,
I have pages, but I am not a bride or royalty;
I have spine and hinges, but I am not a man or a
door,
I have told you all. I cannot tell you more.

John Cunliffe

Answer: A book

*The PS Room

Here I am, sitting in the PS room,
Trying to write a poem.
Everybody is silent, or nearly so.
I can hear someone whispering.
Someone else laughs. The teacher frowns at
him and he blushes.
Everything is quiet again.
Only the rustle of paper as a page is turned.
I notice the *Encyclopaedia Britannica* has
been installed,
Probably for 'the general good and education
of all students'.
I flick through one volume and read
the history of the motor-cycle.
Bored, I put it back on the shelf,
Filling in the hole I had made.

Anthony Halliwell

*PS stands for Physical Science

Lmntl

'Albert, have you a turtle?'
I'll say to him, and Bert'll
say 'Yes! Of *course* I have a turtle.'

But if I write
'Have you a trtl, Albert?'
(as I might)
I wonder if Brtl guess
just what I mean?

We all have seen
a dog's tail wagl,
haven't we?
We all agree
that what a dogldo,
a polywogl too.

We've hrd a brd, grls gigl;
observed how skwrls hnt
for nuts; how big pigs grnt;
know how we feel
on hearing young pigsqweel.

Bbbbs buzz, and ktns play;
bats flitrfly azootowls cry.

Why don't we *spell* that way?
Make ibx look like gnu?
Lfnts too; zbras inizoo?
I do. Do you?

David McCord

Write a Poem

'Write a poem,' our teacher said.
'A poem about an animal or place,
Something that has happened to you
In the holidays.
Better still, write about yourself,
What you feel like,
What's inside you
And wants to come out.'
Stephen straight away
Began to write slowly
And went on and on
Without looking up.
John sighed and looked far away
Then suddenly snatched up his pen
And was scribbling and scribbling.
Ann tossed back her long hair
And smiled as she began.
But I sat still.
I thought of fighting cats
With chewed ears
And dogs sniffing their way along
Windy streets strewn with paper
But there seemed nothing new
To say about them . . .
The holidays? Nothing much happened.
And what's inside me?
Only the numbness of cold fingers,
The grey of the sky today.
John sighed again.
Peter coughed.
Papers rustled.
Pens scratched.

A blowfly was fuzzing
At a window pane.
The tittering clock
Kept snatching the minutes away,
I had nothing to say.

Olive Dunn

Riddle

We are very little creatures
All of different voice and features;
One of us in glAss is set,
One of us you'll find in jEt,
T'other you may see in tIn,
And the fourth a bOx within,
If the fifth you would pursue,
It can never fly from yoU.

Jonathan Swift

Answer: The vowels

Schoolpoem 2

One day i went into the school library and
there were no books. Panic-stricken
i looked for explanations in the eyes
of a school-tied librarian but
she just stamped a date on my wrist
and said i was overdue.
Then i spied one little book called
'HOW TO SPELL'
but
i new how to do that already,
so i sat feeling pretty lonely
as you can imagine in a bookless library,
in the skeleton of a library,
going over all the names of books i once new:
WAR AND PEACE
DANNY THE DORMOUSE
how nice and neat and safe they were.
Now all i do is look for answers
in my blazer pockets but
they have gone through the holes
made by yesterday's
marbles.

Brian McCabe

Arithmetic

I'm 11. And I don't really know
my Two Times Table. Teacher says it's disgraceful
But even if I had the time, I feel too tired.
Ron's 5, Samantha's 3, Carole's 18 months,
and then there's Baby. I do what's required.

Mum's working. Dad's away. And so
I dress them, give them breakfast. Mrs Russell
moves in, and I take Ron to school.
Miss Eames calls me an old-fashioned word: Dunce.
Doreen Maloney says I'm a fool.

After tea, to the Rec. Pram-pushing's slow
but on fine days it's a good place, full
of larky boys. When 6 shows on the clock
I put the kids to bed. I'm free for once.
At about 7 – Mum's key in the lock.

Gavin Ewart

Six Times One

Is six times one a lot of fun?
Or eight times two?
Perhaps for you.
But five times three
Unhinges me,
While six and seven and eight times eight
Put me in an awful state
And four and six and nine times nine
Make me want to cry and whine
So when I get to twelve times ten
I begin to wonder when
I can take a vacation from multiplication
And go out
And start playing again.

Karla Kuskin

In the Garden

Twice one are two,
Violets white and blue.

Twice two are four,
Sunflowers at the door.

Twice three are six,
Sweet peas on their sticks.

Twice four are eight,
Poppies at the gate.

Twice five are ten,
Pansies bloom again.

Twice six are twelve,
Pinks for those who delve.

Twice seven are fourteen,
Flowers of the runner bean.

Twice eight are sixteen,
Clinging ivy ever green.

Twice nine are eighteen,
Purple thistles to be seen.

Twice ten are twenty,
Hollyhocks in plenty.

Twice eleven are twenty-two,
Daisies wet with morning dew.

Twice twelve are twenty-four,
Roses, who could ask for more.

Anon

The Painful Way to Multiply

The teacher viewed the infant boy
Without the slightest sense of joy,
For still he could not calculate
The simple sum of six times eight.

The teacher ranted angrily,
Then took the lad across his knee
And vowed to teach him with a cane
The way to multiply, with pain.

He gave the boy
  six of the best,
But would not let
  the matter rest,
And beat him six times
  more and then
He beat him six times
  once again.

And thus, in multiples
  of six,
Between the pupil's
  cries and kicks,
The teacher could well
  demonstrate
That six times eight
  is forty-eight.

Colin West

1 × 2 is 2

1 × 2 is 2
2 × 2 are 4
3 × 2 are 9
4 × 2 are 17
5 × 2 are 26
6 × 2 are 39
7 × 2 are 148
8 × 2 are 2,204
9 × 2 are 330,916
10 × 2 are 999,999
11 × 2 are 5,222,506½
12 × 2 are 135,926,201⅞

and if anyone says it isn't
meet me in the play ground
tomorrow at high noon,
and don't be late!...

Paul Johnson

Hullo, Inside

Physical-education slides
Show us shots of our insides.
Every day I pat my skin,
'Thanks for keeping it all in.'

Max Fatchen

Science

Science is a world of fun,
They tell me it's a joy;
Explaining all the universe
To every girl and boy.

Zinc Hydroxide, Sodium Chloride, Protons,
 Photons, Quartz!
With names like these to conjure with, who needs
 thoughts?

I've studied all the elements
From arsenic to zinc;
But when it comes to using them
My brain goes on the blink.

Zinc Hydroxide, Sodium Chloride, Napthalene
 and Lime;
Manganese Bromide, Silver Halide, it gets worse all
 the time!

The teachers ask me questions,
'How much, how far, and when?'
I wish they'd try the simple ones
like 'What's fifteen and ten?'

Zinc Hydroxide, Sodium Chloride, Hydrogen and
 Chrome;
If this is what it's leading to I'd rather stay at home.

I've played around with bunsen flames
And test tubes and retorts,
I've mixed up moles and molecules
Of eighty different sorts.

Zinc Hydroxide, Sodium Chloride, Rheostats and
Pi,
I suppose I should be doing this but I really don't
know why!

I've tested reactivities
Of Gallium and Tin;
But I still can't quite figure out
What caused the mess I'm in.

Carbon Monoxide, Sodium Fluoride, Mercury and
Lead;
I wonder why this Science gives me such an aching
head?

Christopher Mann

A Survey of Sovereigns

William, William, Henry the First,
Stephen and Henry the Second;

Richard and John, sir, and Henry the Third,
Then one, two, three Edwards, 'tis reckoned.

Richard the Second and Henry the Fourth,
And Henrys the Fifth and the Sixth, sir;

Edward the Fourth and young Edward the Fifth,
Then Richard or Crooked King Dick, sir.

Henry the Seventh and Henry the Eighth,
Then Edward, then Mary was queen, sir.

Elizabeth, James, then Kings Charles One and
  Two,
(With Oliver Cromwell between, sir).

James, William & Mary, then following Anne,
Four Georges, one after another;

Then William, Victoria, Edward and George
To Edward, who said, 'Crown my brother.'

Colin West

The School at the Top of the Tree

Mr Beecher, the history teacher,
Kept his school at the top of a tree.
The children came from miles around
For his lessons were fun and his classes were free.

Mr Beecher, the history teacher,
Told them tales of battles long done,
Of kings and princes, in war and peace,
Great glories the world had known.

As they listened and dreamed, through the green,
leafy days,
Swaying in the summer sun,
Brave heroes haunted the top of the tree –
They loved them, every one;

Poor Harold dead with an arrow in his eye,
Lord Nelson ruling the waves,
Joan of Arc, with her heart on fire,
Wilberforce freeing the slaves.

Mr Beecher, the history teacher,
Had stories to suit every mood.
But the winds sprang up and the leaves whirled high
As winter stalked through the wood.

Then all who heard his golden tongue
Were the forest creatures wild,
A frozen crow and a long-legged hare –
And one last starving child.

Mr. Beecher, the history teacher,
Climbed down from the top of his tree,
Held out his hand to that cold little boy –
And took him home to tea.

Jenny Craig

Millicent and the Nature Ramble

Millicent Mary liked going to school
For her teachers were really quite nice.
They made lessons pleasant, sometimes even fun,
Except Mr Oliver Price.
He was, truth to tell, a peculiar chap
With a passion for ancient Greek culture
And with his hunched back and his bald, bony head,
He looked like an under-fed vulture.

If Milly was mentioned by one of the staff
He would raise up his eyebrows and groan,
Appealing to heaven to spare him this child
Who seemed to be accident prone.
One has to confess, Mr Price had a point,
And one day he even resolved
To hang out the flags when some mishap occurred
In which Milly wasn't involved.

One day the headmaster announced to the school
That plans had been made to arrange
A nature trail ramble for Millicent's class,
He was sure they would welcome the change.
Mother Nature, he said, could be seen at first hand
They could learn from the country at large
But cries of excitement were very soon stilled
When he said Mr Price was in charge.

On the evening preceding the day of the walk
While playing outside on her swing
Milly saw, on the furthermost part of the lawn
A perfectly formed fairy ring.
A circle of toadstools that peeped through the grass
As if they'd been purposely planted
And Millicent knew if she stood in the ring
Any wish that she made would be granted.

So, closing her eyes as she stood in the ring
And crossing her fingers as well,
She begged any fairy who might be close by
To weave her a small magic spell.
'I don't want too much,' Milly whispered aloud,
'But I'm wishing as hard as can be,
If something goes wrong and annoys Mr Price
Please fairies, don't let it be me.'

Before they set off on the walk the next day
Mr Price scowled grimly at Milly
And rumbled, 'Now Millicent, stay close to me
And please – don't do anything silly.'
Millicent made a rude face at his back
Which I know you may think isn't nice
But one can forgive such a small lapse as that
Especially with teachers like Price.

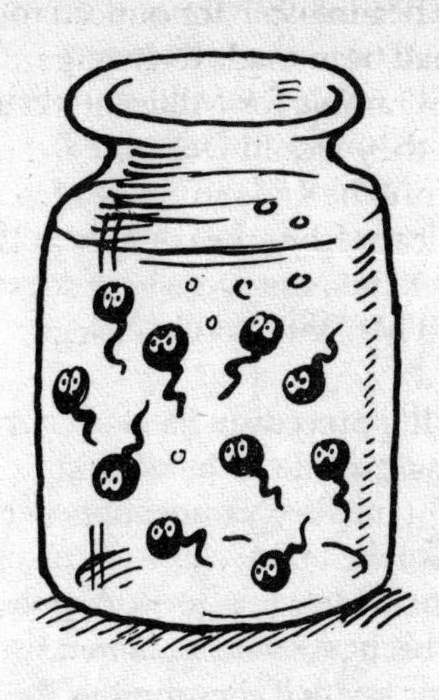

The class wandered off through the woods by the
  church
Inspecting each new plant and flower.
Milly's wish had been granted, for all had gone well
And the class had been out for an hour,
So Milly confided in Angela Brown
She was under the fairies' protection
And Oliver Price, who had heard the remark,
Wandered in Milly's direction.

'Dear child,' he remarked in a sarcastic tone,
'Kindly address your attention
To matters in hand and of fairies and such
I prefer to hear no further mention.'
With that he reached out for a wild primrose flower
As if to examine the petals
And then, quite surprisingly, stumbled headfirst
Into a large clump of nettles.

It was all that the children could do not to laugh
As Mr Price rose looking flustered
And trying to conceal just how foolish he felt
He angrily bellowed and blustered.
Urging the children to hurry along
And threatening to punish their laughter
He strode down the path, still muttering with rage,
As the tittering children ran after.

They came to a stream and a small wooden bridge,
Mr Price made the children go first
Then made to cross over but slipped and fell in –
It seemed like the poor man was cursed.
For each time he tried to get out up the bank
He seemed to meet some strange resistance
And kept falling back, despite half the class
Rushing to give their assistance.

The class were in raptures and laughed till they cried
As back to the school they all straggled
With Oliver Price squelching slowly behind
Looking livid and sorely bedraggled.
He felt like a fool and he looked one as well
As he stood in the staffroom – still draining,
Soaking the carpet to such an extent
That the headmaster started complaining.

Millicent Mary and all of the class
Could hardly believe what they'd seen.
It was almost as if some invisible force
Had pushed Mr Price in the steam.
So take my advice, don't scoff at this tale,
An experience like Millicent Mary's
Might happen to you and it's safer by far
To believe there are such things as fairies.

Doug Millband

My Picture

My flame-picture painting
is pinned on the wall
and teacher says
it's a rainbow ball.

But though I'm pleased
I sometimes frown –
Dare I tell her today
it's upside down?

Archie Barrett

Art

Art is messy,
Paint everywhere.
Paint on the tables,
Paint on the chairs.
Paint on the desk lids,
Paint on the door.
Paint on the ceiling,
Paint on the floor.
Everyone likes Art,
What a merry caper;
There's paint all around the room,
But none on the paper!

Olivia Frances Hum (aged 9)

How to Paint the Portrait of a Bird

First paint a cage
with an open door
then paint
something pretty
something simple
something fine
something useful
for the bird
next place the canvas against a tree
in a garden
in a wood
or in a forest
hide behind the tree
without speaking
without moving . . .
Sometimes the bird comes quickly
but it can also take many years
before making up its mind
Don't be discouraged
wait
wait if necessary for years
the quickness or the slowness of the coming
of the bird having no relation
to the success of the picture
When the bird comes
if it comes
observe the deepest silence
wait for the bird to enter the cage
and when it has entered
gently close the door with the paint-brush
then
one by one paint out all the bars
taking care not to touch one feather of the bird

Next make a portrait of the tree
choosing the finest of its branches
for the bird
paint also the green leaves and the freshness of the
  wind
dust in the sun
and the sound of the insects in the summer grass
and wait for the bird to decide to sing
If the bird does not sing
it is a bad sign
a sign that the picture is bad
but if it sings it is a good sign
a sign that you are ready to sign
so then you pluck very gently
one of the quills of the bird
and you write your name in a corner of the picture.

Jacques Prévert,
(*translated from the French by Paul Dehn*)

Singing

The children are singing,
their mouths open like sleepy fish.
Our teacher conducting the class
waves her arms
like a rhyme in water.
The girls sing high:
our ears ring for the sweetness.
Listeners stand in dazzling amazement.

Peter Sheton (aged 10)

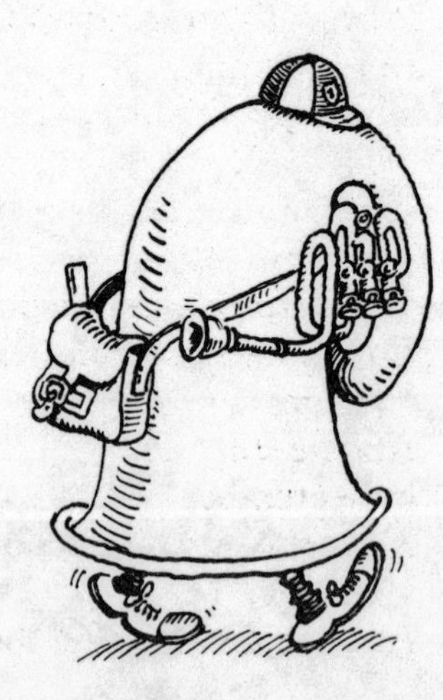

The High School Band

On warm days in September the high school band
Is up with the birds and marches along our street,
Boom boom,
To a field where it goes boom boom until eight
  forty-five
When it marches, as in the old rhyme, back, boom
  boom,
To its study halls, leaving our street
Empty except for the leaves that descend, to no
  drum,
And lie still.
In September
A great many high school bands beat a great many
  drums,
And the silences after their partings are very deep.

Reed Whittemore

Keeping the Score

They're going in to bat: Number One, Number
  Two . . .
It's a long walk to the wicket.
I wonder if he knows his pads are on the wrong
way round?
Where's my pencil? Anybody seen my pencil?
I've got to have one, I'm scoring . . .

Two runs.
No ball.

Two runs, no ball, one run. Two runs, no ball,
one run . . . Where *is* that pencil?
He's out! Can I borrow a pencil? Thank you, sir,
yes, sir; I'll give it back afterwards.
Two runs, no ball, one run . . . out.

It's a very long walk to the wicket.
Even longer back.
The sun's hot.
Bet it's hot out there.

Why are umpires always fat?

Now the point's broken! Why does it always
  happen to me?
Howzat!
Wait, my pencil's broken!
Sir, can I have another pencil? No, sir, I didn't
do it deliberately, sir, it just went . . .

Maiden over. That's an 'M', I think.

I wonder how high that cloud is?

Another maiden.

Wish I could sit under the trees. It's hot.

The fat umpire's got his coat on and two sweaters
round his neck. Why doesn't *he* get hot?

One run.

I wonder if anyone would mind if I went and scored
under the trees?

This pencil's too thick. What'll I do if it breaks?
I can't ask Sir again.

Howzat! Not out.

One day I'll fly a plane like that: so high up all
you can see is its trail.

I wonder where it's going.

Out!

Who's number four?

Come on, number four, where are you?

Crikey, it's me!

Score! Somebody score!

Who cares about the pencil . . . where's my bat?

Christopher Mann

Friday Morning Last Two Lessons is Games Day

We straggle in two's
Down Enbutt Lane to the playing fields
In a gap-toothed murmuring line
Filling the pavement.
Mr Pearson strides out in front
The ball tucked firmly under one arm,
His head bent.

We avoid lampposts
And young mothers pushing prams,
Sometimes walk gammy-legged in gutters
Or scuffle through damp leaves.
The morning is filled
With laughter-tongued and pottering mongrels;
Old men tending bare borders
Slowly unbend
And lean upon their brooms to watch us pass.
Their wives in flowered pinnies
Peer through the lace curtains
Of unused front rooms.

At the pitch
We change in the old pavilion
That smells of dust and feet
And has knot holes in the boarding.
Someone
From another class
Has left
One
Blue and white sock behind.

The lads shout about other games
And goals and saves and shots
Or row about who'll wear red or blue
Pearson blows exasperation
'Come on, lads, let's be having you

With eighteen a side
We tear after the ball shouting,
Longing to give it a good clean belt,
Perform some piece of perfection –
Beat three sprawling backs in a mazy dribble,
Race full pelt on to a plate-laid-on pass
And crack it full of hate and zest
Past the diving goalie to bulge the net.
But there is no net
And we have to leg it after the ball
To the allotments by the lane
Before we can take centre
To start the game again.

Afterwards,
Still wearing football socks,
Studded boots slung on my shoulder,
I say 'Tarrah' to Trev
At Station Road and drift home
Playing the game again.
Smoke climbs up from the neat red chimneys;
Babies drool and doze
And laugh at the empty sky.
There is the savour of cabbage and gravy
About the Estate and the flowers do not hear
The great crowd roaring me on.

Gareth Owen

Winter Sports

It's freezing outside and there's snow on the
  ground,
But the games master's leaping and dancing around.
He thinks that it's fun to be frozen and blue
And he wants to play football, so what can we do?
IS HE MAD?? Is he drunk? Has he got a screw
  loose?
We search high and low to find some excuse.

But alas none appears. To the pitches we jog,
And begin to play football. Not easy in fog.
Knees knock together, fingers turn blue,
The games master's yelling, he's passing to you,
'Run with the ball, boy, dribble and score,'
But there's snow in your boots and you can't take
  much more.

We've tried to play football, we've all done our best,
Now send for the husky dogs, skis and the rest.
Still the games master says that we've not had
  enough,
'You'll stay so that people can see that you're
  tough.'
But there'll be some surprise when they see through
  the mist
Twenty-two little snowmen and one waving his
  fist.

Charles Davies

A Wet Football Game

Wet and muddy, soaked right through,
 Covered with bruises, black, red and blue.
Socks at ankles, laces flying,
 I really almost feel like crying.
But wait a minute, did we win?
 How many goals did we get in?
More or less than the opposition?
 I can't remember my position.
Was I in goal or was I attack?
 I remember now – I was Left Back
Yes, we won by eight to two
 I'm glad my first football game is through!

Anon

Kevin Scores!

Kevin flicks the ball sideways, leaning
From it, letting it roll
Away, smoothly. He knows Tom is sprinting
Up from defence for it, down
The touchline, so he moves seriously beyond
The centre-half, hoping the ball will come
Over, perfectly, within the reach
Of his timed leap, so he can dive upward,
Feet pointed, arms balancing,
Arched like a hawk for the stab of his head at the
goal.

He has seen it often, Law,
And Osgood on the telly,
How they wait hungrily
Under the ball floating over,
Then the great poise of the leap,
Almost too late you'd think,
Like great cats hunting,
Or sleek, muscular sharks,
Leaping beyond gravity, up, up,
Then the sharp snap of the head
And the white ball coldly in the net.

Kevin waits by the far post, willing
Tom to get the ball over.
He feels slack and alone, he can see
David in goal, elbows tensely bent, fingers
Stretched for catching in his old woollen gloves.
Tom sways inside the back, he takes
Two short steps, he swings
His left foot, and the ball lifts
Perfectly, perfectly,
Within the bound of Kevin's timed leap.
He is drawn to it, he straightens
In a slow upward dive, and he bends back,
Eyes rapt on the crossed ball he rises
To meet, and now
The sharp snap of his head
And the white ball coldly past the plunging David.

As he runs downfield he knows his face is laughing.

Leslie Norris

Jolly Hockey Sticks!

Elaine and I would crouch at the back.
If picked for the team our nerve would crack.
'Elaine, centre back. Teresa, left wing.
Get on your feet and give it some zing.'

Bully off, bully off! Why am I here?
Crikey! The ball's getting horribly near.
Brenda Stokes is waving her stick.
If she gets any closer I'll give her a kick.

I can't take any more of this grizzly game.
It's enough to make you wish you were lame.
What heavenly music! The whistle's blowing.
And that's the end of this pitiful poem.

Louise Draycott

Homework

'I'm not going to do my homework!'
I said, yesterday, with glee,
Boasting to friends as we made our way home.
'Why don't *you* skip it, like me?'

'I don't want to do my homework!'
Mother ignored my plea:
'Hurry up and finish eating,
Do your homework after tea.'

I can't concentrate on homework
With the family watching TV.
I pretended I had finished.
Mother didn't ask to see.

How I wished I had done my homework
As friends showed their books to me.
I *knew* I'd get into trouble –
Blank pages where my work should be!

Tonight I *will* do my homework.
Teachers always win, you see.
They made me miss swimming to complete it.
Tonight I'll do it *before* tea.

Marian Gosling

I Love to do my Homework

I love to do my homework.
It makes me feel so good.
I love to do exactly
As my teacher says I should.

I love to do my homework,
I never miss a day.
I even love the men in white
Who are taking me away.

Anon

The Last Exam
A villanelle

A villanelle was a round song sung by French farmers in the Middle Ages.

To read the questions carefully
I hold my breath like a balloon.
After this one I'll be free

of European History,
of desks and people in this room,
after this one I'll be free.

'In the thirteenth century . . .'
It's much too hot this afternoon
to read the questions carefully.

I watch them scribble busily
as if there were no flaming June . . .
after this one I'll be free

to fish and swim down by the sea,
to lie and dream or watch the moon.
To read the questions carefully,

and answer them, I have to be
a wingless bug in a cocoon.
After this one I'll be free

to fly and make some history.
So I begin, in silent gloom,
to read the questions carefully.
After this one I'll be free.

Jane Whittle

Bad Report – Good Manners

My daddy said, 'My son, my son,
This school recport is bad.'
I said, 'I did my best I did,
My dad my dad my dad.'
'Explain, my son, my son,' he said,
'Why *bottom* of the class?'
'I stood aside, my dad my dad,
To let the others pass.'

Spike Milligan

School Report

'TOO EASILY SATISFIED. SPELLING STILL
POOR.
HER GRAMMAR'S ERRATIC. LACKS CARE.
WOULD SUCCEED IF SHE WORKED.
INCLINED TO BE SMUG.'
I think that's a wee bit unfare.

Ah well, their it is! Disappointing perhaps,
For a mum what has always had brane,
But we can't all have looks or be good at our
books . . .
She's her father all over agane.

Carole Paine

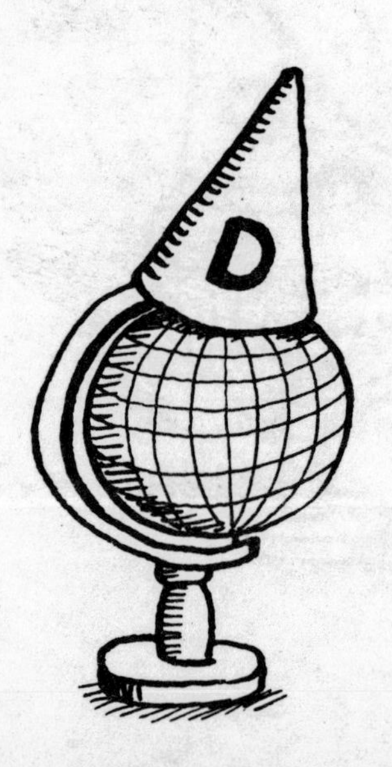

IN THE PLAYGROUND

Morning break

Andrew Flag plays football
Jane swings from the bars
Chucker Peach climbs drainpipes
Spike is seeing stars

Little Paul's a Martian
Anne walks on her toes
Ian Dump fights Kenny
Russell picks his nose

Dopey Di does hop-scotch
Curly drives a train
Maddox-Brown and Thompson
Stuff shoes down the drain

Lisa Thin throws netballs
Mitchell stands and stares
Nuttall from the first year
Shouts and spits and swears

Dick Fish fires his ray gun
Gaz has stamps to swop
Dave and Dan are robbers
Teacher is the cop

Betty Blob pulls faces
Basher falls . . . and dies
Tracey shows her knickers
Loony swallows flies

Faye sits in a puddle
Trev is eating mud
Skinhead has a nose bleed
– pints and pints of blood

Robbo Lump pings marbles
Murray hands out cake
What a lot of nonsense
During
  Morning
    Break

Wes Magee

In the Playground

In the playground
Some run round
Chasing a ball
Or chasing each other;
Some pretend to be
Someone on TV;
Some walk
And talk,
Some stand
On their hands
Against the wall
And some do nothing at all.

Stanley Cook

Complaint

The teachers all sit in the staffroom.
The teachers all drink tea.
The teachers all smoke cigarettes
As cosy as can be.

We have to go out at playtime
Unless we bring a note
Or it's tipping down with rain
Or we haven't got a coat.

We have to go out at playtime
Whether we like it or not.
And freeze to death if it's freezing
And boil to death if it's hot.

The teachers can sit in the staffroom
And have a cosy chat.
We have to go out at playtime;
Where's the fairness in that?

Allan Ahlberg

Skipping Songs

The High Skip,
The Sly Skip,
The Skip like a Feather,
The Long Skip,
The Strong Skip,
And the Skip All Together.

The Slow Skip,
The Toe Skip,
The Skip Double-Double
The Fast Skip,
The Last Skip,
And the Skip Against Trouble.

One I love, two I loathe,
Three I cast away;
Four I love with all my heart,
Five I love, I *say*.
Six he loves me, seven he don't,
Eight he'll marry me, nine he won't,
Ten he would if he could, but he can't,
Eleven he comes, twelve he tarries,
Thirteen he's waiting, fourteen he marries.

I took my girl to a ball one night
And sat her down to supper,
The table fell and she fell too,
And stuck her nose in the butter.

Traditional

Skipping Song

Anne and Belinda
Turning the rope,
Helen jumps in
But she hasn't got a hope.
Helen Freckles
What will you do
Skip on the table
In the Irish Stew.
Freckles on her face
Freckles on her nose
Freckles on her knee caps
Freckles on her toes.

Helen Freckles
Tell me true
How many freckles have you got on you?
One, two, three, four, five, six . . .
And out goes you.

Stella Starwars
Skip in soon
In your spaceship
And off to the moon.
Skip on the pavement
One and two
Skip like a rabbit
Or a kangaroo;
Skip so high
You'll never come down;
Over the steeple
Over the town.
Skip over roof tops
Skip over trees
Skip over rivers
Skip over seas,
Skip over London
Skip over Rome
Skip all night
And never come home.
Skip over moonbeams
Skip over Mars
Skip through the Milky Way
And try to count the stars.
One, two, three, four, five, six . . .
And out goes you.

Gareth Owen
(from 'Skipping Song')

Counting-out Rhymes

Inty, tinty, tethery, methery,
Bank for over, Dover, ding,
Aut, taut, toosh;
Up the Causey, down the Cross,
There stands a bonnie white horse:
It can gallop, it can trot,
It can carry the mustard pot.
One, two, three, out goes she!

One-ery, two-ery, dickery, dee.
Halibo, crickbo, dandilee;
Pin, pan, myskee dan,
Tweddledum, twaddledum, twenty-one;
Black fish, white trout.
Eeny, meeny, you go out.

Hoky poky, winky wum,
How do you like your 'taters done?
Snip, snap, snorum,
High popolorum,
Kate go scratch it,
You are out.

Icker-backer
Soda-cracker
Icker-backer-boo
En-gine
Number nine
Out go you.

Traditional

Counting-out Rhyme

Silver bark of beech, and sallow
Bark of yellow birch and yellow
  Twig of willow.

Stripe of green in moosewood maple,
Colour seen in leaf of apple,
  Bark of popple.

Wood of popple pale as moonbeam,
Wood of oak for yoke and barn-beam,
  Wood of hornbeam.

Silver bark of beech, and hollow
Stem of elder, tall and yellow
  Twig of willow.

Edna St Vincent Millay

The Blue Ball

With many a bump
On the bouncy ground
Quiet and gentle
We pass it round;
Till Jennifer stumbles,
Sally-Ann fumbles,
And look, it's over
The playground wall!
PLEASE-WILL-YOU-THROW-US-BACK-
  OUR-BALL?

Back now it comes.
Jimbo catches it
And holds it fast
Till Martin snatches it;
He throws to Tom,
Who, all unready,
Lets it go by;
It's caught by Teddy.
Teddy will keep it
As long as he can –
Toss it and bounce it;
But quickly Ann
Cries, 'Drop it you silly!'
In rushes Billy
And *kicks* it over
The playground wall!
PLEASE-WILL-YOU-THROW-US-BACK-
  OUR-BALL?

But close and sly
By the playground gate,
Big Bill Craddock
He lies in wait.
Straight to his feet
The blue ball bounces;
Bill Craddock leaps on it,
Bill Craddock pounces.
Look! Off he goes with it –
Cutting mad capers,
Does all he knows with it
Wild to escape us;
Turns a fierce grin
To the tongues that would scold him;
Tears himself free
From the hands that would hold him;

Uses his cunning
At tripping and running,
Turns about twistily,
Fights with his fist till he
Holds the ball high
And with a great cry
He *hurls* it over
The playground wall!
PLEASE-WILL-YOU-THROW-US-BACK-
OUR-BALL?

John Walsh

Ball Bouncing Rhymes

Queen Caroline

Queen, Queen Caroline,
Dipped her hair in turpentine;
Turpentine made it shine,
Queen, Queen Caroline.

Through the Teeth

Through the teeth
And past the gums
Look out stomach,
Here it comes!

Order in the Court

Order in the court
The judge is eating beans
His wife is in the bath tub
Shooting submarines

Traditional

Whip Top

Whip top! Whip top!
Turn about and never stop!
Monday's top will spin away,
Tuesday's top will sing all day,
Wednesday's top is never slow,
Thursday's top to sleep will go,
Friday's top will dance about,
Saturday's top will tire you out!
Whip top! Whip top!
Spin around and never stop!

Anon

Conkers

When chestnuts are hanging
Above the school yard,
They are little green sea-mines
Spiky and hard.

But when they fall bursting
And all the boys race,
Each shines like a jewel
In a satin case.

Clive Sansom

Down in the Meadow

Down in the meadow
Where the green grass grows,
To see Sally Waters
Bloom like a rose:
Sally made a pudding,
She made it so sweet,
And never stuck a knife in
Till Johnny came to eat.
Taste love, taste love,
And don't say nay,
For next Monday morning
Is your wedding day.
He bought her a gown
And a guinea-gold ring,
And a fine cocked hat
To be married in.

Northampton playground game

The Alley-Alley-O

The big ship sails through the Alley-Alley-O
the Alley-Alley-O, Alley-Alley-O,
The ship sails through the Alley-Alley-O
on the last day of December!

Traditional

School

Bang! Slap! Punch!
Those two are having a fight.
One of them swings a nice left hook
The other swings a right.
The teacher comes to stop the fight –
And accidentally takes the right.

Patrick McCoy

Back in the Playground Blues

Dreamed I was in a school playground, I was about
four feet high
Yes dreamed I was back in the playground and
standing about four feet high
The playground was three miles long and the
playground was five miles wide

It was broken black tarmac with a high fence all
around
Broken black dusty tarmac with a high fence
running all around
And it had a special name to it, they called it The
Killing Ground.

Got a mother and a father, they're a thousand miles
away
The Rulers of the Killing Ground are coming out to
play
Everyone thinking: who they going to play with
today?

You get it for being Jewish
Get it for being black
Get it for being chicken
Get it for fighting back
You get it for being big and fat
Get it for being small
O those who get it get it and get it
For any damn thing at all

Sometimes they take a beetle, tear off its six legs one
by one
Beetle on its black back rocking in the lunchtime
sun
But a beetle can't beg for mercy, a beetle's not half
the fun

Heard a deep voice talking, it had that iceberg
sound;
'It prepares them for Life' – but I have never found
Any place in my life that's worse than The Killing
Ground.

Adrian Mitchell

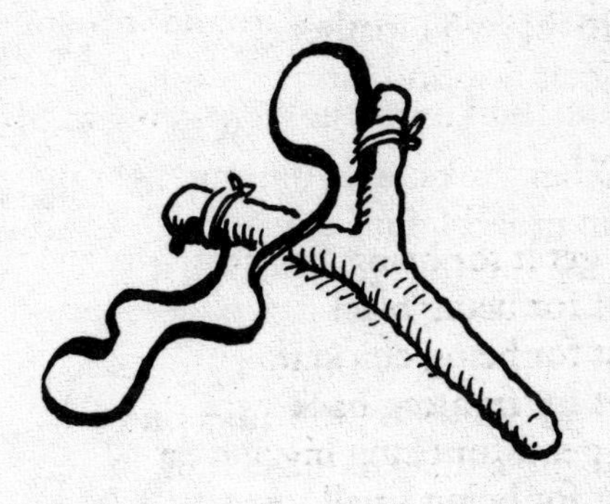

Winter Playground

In the cold winter sunshine
The children stand against the wall.
They look like washing on a line,

Neat red coat, stripey mitts,
Narrow green tights with a hole in the knee.
Still and stiff, frozen in a row.

Across the playground
Three boys are chasing a ball.
A little dog barks through the fence.

A skipping rope curves –
'One I love, two I loathe . . .'
As the girls hop and jump.

The teacher stalks, eyes darting,
Scattering marbles in his way,
Keeping a look-out for TROUBLE.

But from the train window
It's the still ones I see, the quiet ones,
Straight and stiff against the wall,
Like washing, frozen on the line.

Jenny Craig

SCHOOL FOOD

Whole Duty of Children

A child should always say what's true,
And speak when he is spoken to
And behave mannerly at table:
At least as far as he is able.

Robert Louis Stevenson

Come to the Cook-house Door

Come to the cook-house door,
Come to the cook-house door,
Fill your belly full of jelly,
Come to the cook-house door.

Traditional

Martha Munch

Martha Munch, Martha Munch,
Why can't you wait like the rest until lunch?
You've nibbled in Needlework,
Guzzled in Games,
Slurped through the Scripture class,
Called us all names.
Are you really so shocked when you see our surprise
As you greedily chew through a batch of pork pies?

Martha Munch, Martha Munch,
Eating bananas by wolfing the bunch.
You ate figs in the first lesson,
Steak in the second,
How much in the third lesson?
No one has reckoned.
The teachers are helpless, we all turn away,
You eat more in one lesson than we do all day.

Martha Munch, Martha Munch,
Why aren't you moving, the bell's gone for lunch?
Martha's trying to say something, trying to speak
But the food in her mouth makes her voice
somewhat weak.
Then we realize with glee just how much we're in
luck
Because Martha has eaten so much that she's stuck.
Trapped at her desk we can leave Martha Munch,
Today for us all there'll be plenty of lunch.

Charles Davies

Dinner Queue Dilemma

The boy stood in the dinner queue
And heaved a great big sigh.
He wondered what to eat today –
Egg and ham? Or pie?
Curry and rice? Or toad-in-the-hole?
Dumpling stew? Or fry?
Chips and beans? *No* horrid greens!
Whatever should he try?

At last he managed to reach the front,
And opened his mouth to speak . . .
'Everything's *off*,' the lady said,
'Except for bubble-and-squeak.'

Timothy Hattersley

School Dinners

If you stay to school dinners
Better throw them aside.
A lot of kids didn't,
A lot of kids died.
The meat is of iron,
The puds are of steel.
If the gravy don't get you,
The custard will.

Traditional

James Bond comes to Lunch

The day James Bond came to lunch at our school
He
Dive bomb'd a sausage
Kung Fu'd a carrot
Machine gunn'd a fish-cake
Swam through the custard
And
Kissed Agnes the dinner lady.

Tom Edwards

School Gravy

'Why don't you *eat*?' the mother said,
'Roast, veg, and Yorkshire pud,
You surely have an appetite?
You can't resist such food!'

A tear slipped down the small boy's face,
He sighed, and shook his head.
'Oh why can't you make gravy
Like they do at school?' he said.

The mother's face went scarlet.
'Mine is beyond compare!
It's meaty, juicy, tasty too,
With flavour rich and rare.'

The small boy nodded sadly.
'I know. I must agree.
But at school it's something *special*.
I . . . like the lumps, you see!'

Jenny Craig

Drinking Fountain

When I climb up
   To get a drink,
It doesn't work
   The way you'd think.

I turn it up.
   The water goes
And hits me right
   Upon the nose.

I turn it down
   To make it small
And don't get any
   Drink at all.

Marchette Chute

Pancake Day

Pancake day is a very happy day,
If we don't have a holiday we'll all run away,
Where shall we run, up High Lane,
And here comes the teacher with a great big cane.

Traditional

A Peanut sat on the Railroad Track

A peanut sat on the railroad track,
His heart was all a-flutter;
Along came a train – the 9.15 –
Toot, toot, peanut butter!

Anon

Through The Teeth

Through the teeth
And past the gums.
Look out, stomach,
Here it comes!

Anon

I Eat My Peas With Honey

I eat my peas with honey.
I've done it all my life.
It makes the peas taste funny
But it keeps 'em on the knife!

Anon

SCHOOL TEACHERS

Distracted the Mother said to her Boy

Distracted the mother said to her boy
'Do you try to upset and perplex and annoy?
Now, give me four reasons – and don't play the
fool –
Why you shouldn't get up and get ready for school.'

Her son replied slowly, 'Well, mother, you see,
I can't stand the teachers and they detest me;
And there isn't a boy or a girl in the place
That I like or, in turn, that delights in my face.'

'And I'll give you two reasons,' she said, 'why you
ought
Get yourself off to school before you get caught;
Because, first, you are forty and, next, you young
fool,
It's your job to be there.
You're the head of the school.'

Gregory Harrison

New Teachers

New teachers
remind me of woodworm,
Just moved into
a new piece of wood.

Anon

Teachers

Teachers get stuck with the subjects they teach.
FRENCH wears wool cardigans, HISTORY's
hair's bleached.

PHYSICS is fat and LATIN goes bald,
R.E. gets flat feet, COOKING cat-calls.

GEOGRAPHY always wears sweaters and jeans,
ART leather jackets with gaps in the seams.

ENGLISH has thick specs and spots and a grin,
CHEMISTRY laughs a lot, MUSIC is thin.

MATHS has a habit of biting his nails,
DRAMA has big eyes and goes off to Wales.

BIOLOGY runs about puffing and shouting,
P.E.'s in the pub on every school outing.

Subjects get stuck to the people who teach them.
The people I like do the subjects I'm keen on.

Jane Whittle

He Who owns the Whistle rules the World

January wind and the sun
playing truant again.
Rain beginning to scratch
its fingernails across
the blackboard sky

in the playground
kids divebomb, corner
at silverstone or execute
traitors. Armed
with my Acme Thunderer
I step outside,
take a deep breath
and bring the world
to a standstill

Roger McGough

Words with Teacher

These are the words that teachers use:
Hypothesis, hypotenuse,
Isosceles, trapezium,
Potassium, magnesium,
Denominator, catechism
And antidisestablishmentarianism.

Colin West

A Close Shave

Another day is on the way
As the pips start ringing in my ear

Oh no! I forgot my letter about the other day
When I was away. Trouble!

She comes walking in the door
She gets closer to the drawer
She gets the register out
She starts to call the names
She gets closer and closer to my name
I'm going to be in trouble
I say yes!
She goes on!
She forgot, forgot, FORGOT!

David Bryant

A Teacher

A teacher's got a temper
like a bull.
He growls and roars
like a tiger,
he stamps and gets mad
and sometimes he's glad
he did it.

Bruce McGregor (aged 11)

A Schoolmaster's Admonition

Good children, refuse not these lessons to learn,
The pathway to virtue you here may discern;
In keeping them truly you shall be most sure
The praise of all people thereby to procure.

Be comely and decent in all thy array,
Not wantonly given to sport and to play;
But labour by virtue, in youth, to obtain
The love of thy betters, their friendship to gain.

The morning appearing, rise thou with speed,
Wash hands and face cleanly before thou go feed;
Let shoes be fast tied both, close to thy feet,
The better to travel all day in the street.

If thou be a scholar, to school make good haste,
For he is a truant that cometh there last;
For if thou dost loiter and play by the way,
Be sure with thy master it will cause a fray.

Swear not, nor curse not; delight not to steal;
Thy master obey thou; his secrets conceal;
Take heed of false lying; set no man at strife;
Nor be thou too desperate to strike with a knife.

And now, to conclude, bear this well in mind,
A diligent scholar much favour shall find;
But such as will loiter, and lazy will be,
Shall for their labour be brought on their knee.

Anon (1625)

Writing Right

Said a boy to his teacher one day,
'Wright has not written 'rite' right, I say!'
And the teacher replied
As the error she eyed:
'Right! – Wright, write 'rite' right, right away!'

Anon

If the Teacher was a Robot

If the teacher was a robot,
Made of Iron and Tin
We could take it all to pieces
And put it in the bin.
We'd loosen all its nuts and bolts
In the metalwork room,
We would weld its mouth tight shut,
And send it to its doom.

Paul Marsh (aged 13)

A Teacher from Harrow

There was a young teacher from Harrow
Whose nose was too long and too narrow.
It gave so much trouble
That he bent it up double
And wheeled it round school in a barrow.

Anon

A Teacher from Leeds

There once was a teacher from Leeds
Who swallowed a packet of seeds.
In less than an hour
Her nose was a flower
And her hair was a posy of weeds.

Anon

Thoughts

All people that on Earth do dwell,
Hope Mr Foster isn't in a bad mood,
Wonder if he's here yet?
Bet he's having his breakfast,
Come ye before him and rejoice.

The piano's wobbly,
Might fall over,
Without our aid he did us make,
Hope Mr Foster's ill,
And for his sheep he doth us take,

O enter then his gates with praise,
Latin room's empty,
Approach with joy his courts unto,
I'm in detention today,
Have to write out 100 lines,
For it is seemly so to do.

Marcus Holburn (aged 10)

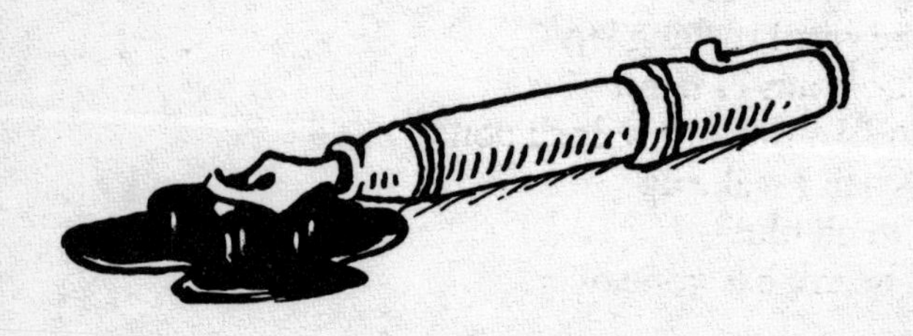

Daydreams

Miss Barter thinks I'm reading,
But I'm taming lions,
or stalking kangaroos . . .
I am on the moon . . .
or swimming under water.
I have a fight with an octopus
and a giant sword fish . . .
I go home late at night
with ten fish
I caught in the river.

Miss Barter thinks I'm listening –
But no.
I'm boxing for the navy . . .
I'm diving off a cliff,
or throwing custard pies
at the circus.
I am a strong man,
big and lumpy . . .
I sit and float
in a big balloon
soaring through the clouds,
floating swiftly.

I think of racing a big train
in a sports car,
the wind rushing by:
I go round a bend
and go through a duck pond! . . .
When I wake up
I'm all blue –
The ink has gone over.

Richard Compton, (aged 10)

Miss Norma Jean Pugh, First Grade Teacher

Full of oatmeal
And gluggy with milk
On a morning in spring time
Soft as silk
When legs feel slow
And bumble bees buzz
And your nose tickles from
Dandelion fuzz
And you long to
Break a few
Cobwebs stuck with
Diamond dew
Stretched right out
In front of you –
When all you want
To do is *feel*
Until it's time for
Another meal,
Or sit right down
In the cool
Green grass
And watch the
Caterpillars pass . . .
Who cares if
Two and two
Are four or five
Or red or blue?

Who cares whether
Six or seven
Come before or after
Ten or eleven?
Who cares if
C – A – T
Spells cat or rat
Or tit or tat
Or ball or bat?
Well, I do
But I didn't
Used to –
Until MISS NORMA JEAN PUGH!
She's terribly old
As people go
Twenty-one-or-five-or-six
Or so
But she makes a person want to
KNOW!

Mary O'Neill

I was Mucking About in Class

I was mucking about in class

Mr Brown said,
Get out and take your chair with me
I suppose he *meant* to say
Take your chair with you
so Dave said,
Yeah – you heard what he said
            get out and take my chair with him
so Ken said,
Yeah – get out and take his chair with me
so I said to Mr Brown
Yessir – shall I take our chair with you, sir?

Wow
that meant BIG TROUBLE

Michael Rosen

SCHOOL PETS AND OTHER PEOPLE

Tashy the School's Rabbit

We clean his play pen
      every day
When we've finished we
      go out to play.
Miss Grundy gives him her
      home-made bread,
Tashy's pram is shining
      red.
Tashy sleeps in his wooden
      hutch
We all love him very
      much.
Tashy's eyes are very bright,
His furry coat is black
      and white.
He goes home with all
      his kind friends,
We wouldn't leave
      him in school at weekends.
Sometimes he's in a
      naughty mood,
But this doesn't put him
      off his food.
Tashy runs and scampers
      free,
When he's tired he sleeps
      on my knee.

If it is warm he goes out
        on the grass,
The children shout, 'Hello'
        as they pass
Carrots, oats and pears he
        loves to eat
He then runs round Miss
        Grundy's feet.
He begs, he searches, he
        jumps on our knees
Just 'cos he's looking
        for dandelion leaves.
At home-time it's into
        his pen and close the door
Tashy settles down and
        sleeps on his straw.

Rachel Teggert (aged 7)

The Goldfish

Jimmy Slater bullied me
And Brian Wilkins laughed at me
But when I was teased
Or lonely
Or sad
I would go to the prefab
Behind the bike sheds but
Before the gym
That housed the aquarium.

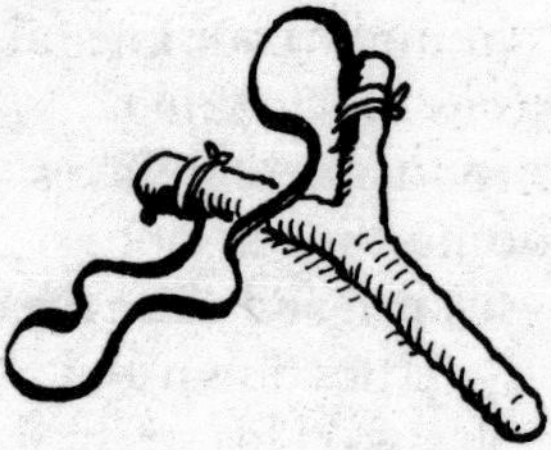

I would sit
Amid the flashing brilliance of the guppies
Under the wise watchful eyes of ancient terrapins
But I would watch the goldfish
Humble and beautiful
Simple and majestic
As it glided through its
Tangled weeds and greenish stones
As unaware as I was
Of the laughing eyes
Watching me
Watching the fish.

Until one day
Feeling low
I came to watch
But found instead
Smashed glass and
A trickle of water from
The bench to the floor.
And there,
Surrounded by the broken shards,
Limp weed trailing over its fin,
Lay the goldfish,
Dazzling in the harsh light.

Tom Edwards

Zebra Crossing

There is a Lollipopman
At the zebra crossing
With lollipops
He is trying
To lure zebras across
He makes me cross.
I cross.

Roger McGough

Lost

Dear Mrs Butler, this is just a note
About our Raymond's coat
Which he came home without last night,
So I thought I'd better write.

He was minus his scarf as well, I regret
To say; and his grandma is most upset
As she knitted it and it's pure
Wool. You'll appreciate her feelings, I'm sure.

Also, his swimming towel has gone
Out of his PE bag, he says, and one
Of his socks, too – it's purplish and green
With a darn in the heel. His sister Jean

Has a pair very similar. And while
I remember, is there news yet of those fairisle
Gloves which Raymond lost that time
After the visit to the pantomime?

Well, I think that's all. I will close now,
Best wishes, yours sincerely, Maureen Howe
(Mrs). PS I did once write before
About his father's hat that Raymond wore

In the school play and later could not find,
But got no reply. Still, never mind,
Raymond tells me now he might have lost the note,
Or left it in the pocket of his coat.

Allan Ahlberg

Mr Fitzsimmons

Mr Fitzsimmons,
Our caretaker, is tall
For reaching pictures
Down from the wall,
Looking over gates
And piled-up crates.
Just the height
To put new bulbs
In electric lights
Or discover
What was lost
On top of cupboards.
He has a key
Worn shiny in his pocket
For every door
And a polisher
Plugging in at the socket
For every floor.
He brushes school clean
And polishes it bright
Every night.

Stanley Cook

Mr Mole

The person I know best at school
stays out of sight as a rule
keeping warm in a dusty old room
with a bucket, a mop and a broom.

If it's too cold to shiver outside
he has let me join him inside
while he brews up his afternoon tea.
He once shared a sandwich with me.

Mr Mole lost a leg in The War
but the wooden one's more useful for
planting out lettuces, he says,
when he does his Allotment on Sundays.

His job is a School Janitor
but he works more at being a gardener,
growing onions, carrots and cabbages.
He refuses to say what his age is.

Mr Mole says the earth and the air
have made him a young millionaire.

Jane Whittle

The School Nurse

We're lining up to see the nurse
And in my opinion there's nothing worse.
It is the thing I always dread.
Supposing I've got *nits* in my head.

I go inside and sit on the chair.
She ruffles her fingers in my hair.
I feel my face getting hot and red.
Supposing she finds *nits* in my head.

It's taking ages; it must be bad.
Oh, how shall I tell my mum and dad?
I'd rather see the dentist instead
Than be the one with *nits* in his head.

Then she taps my arm and says, 'Next please!'
And I'm out in the corridor's cooling breeze.
Yet still I can feel that sense of dread.
Supposing she *had* found nits in my head.

Allan Ahlberg

After Adrian Mitchell – We Liked His Stuff!

You came up from London with it.
Came into our school with it.
POETRY
We liked your stuff!

You took all your books from it.
We got lots of laughs from it.
POEM BAG
We liked your stuff!

For your birthday you were given it.
Took it off when you got hot in it.
LEATHER JACKET
We liked your stuff!

Many a cat was killed by it.
Everyone was filled by it.
CURIOSITY
We liked your stuff!

All your poems are printed on it.
Some are still in scribbles on it.
PAPER
We liked your stuff!

You failed your exams for it.
Our mums and dads all danced to it.
ROCK AND ROLL
We liked your stuff!

Lines in your poems created it.
Children burst right out with it.
LAUGHTER
We liked your stuff!

Excitement in the classroom –
Ideas in our head –
Creating, thinking, writing –
We were the poets instead.
For you we created them.
Then we went away with them.
POEMS
Because we liked your stuff!

Class 9, Tyldesly County
Primary School

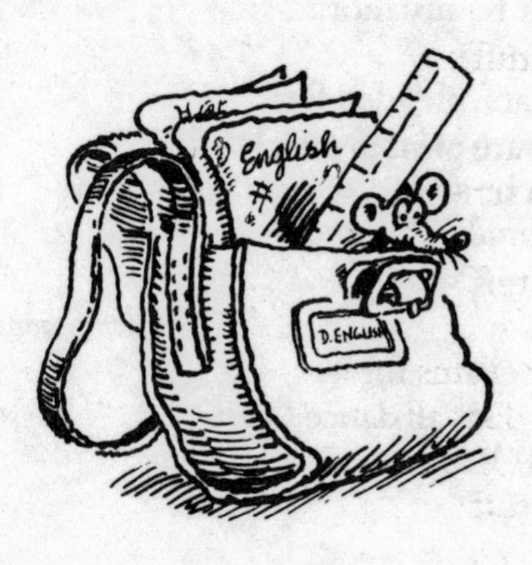

Intelligence Test

'What do you use your eyes for?'
The white-coated man enquired.
'I use my eyes for looking,'
Said Toby, – 'unless I'm tired.'

'I see. And then you close them,'
Observed the white-coated man.
'Well done. A very good answer.
Let's try another one.

What is your nose designed for?
What use is the thing to you?'
'I use my nose for smelling,'
Said Toby, 'Don't you, too?'

'I do indeed,' said the expert,
'That's what the thing is for.
Now I've another question to ask you,
Then there won't be any more.

'What are your ears intended for?
Those things at each side of your head?
Come on – don't be shy – I'm sure you can say.'
'For washing behind,' Toby said.

Vernon Scannell

Aristotle and Ballcocks

They sent me to see the careers man,
He was in a posh office down town,
I tried to be pleasant and friendly,
But all I received was a frown.

'I'm sorry to have to inform you,
But it takes more than three CSEs,
Especially as one is in woodwork,
And the others are only grade threes,

'It takes years of hard work to be one,
Philosophers aren't trained they are born,
And besides your "qualifications",
There isn't a box on the form.'

So he sent me away with a leaflet,
To get on a GYOS*
By the time I walked home from the bus stop,
I thought, 'Oh hell, what a mess!'

When I told my dad, he couldn't stop laughing,
His face went all purple and red,
And when he recovered from choking,
He told me, 'Try plumbing instead,'

So I looked it up on my leaflet,
And filled in the space on the form,
I read up on ballcocks and U-bends,
And reflected the fate of a pawn.

If Descartes had had this problem,
And Aristotle and Socrates too,
We might not have had great thinkers,
But just think of the showers and loos!

So I went back to see the careers man,
Who said, 'It's a safer idea,
To stick to something more normal,
A job and not a career.'

Emma Payne (aged 15)

**Government Youth Opportunity Scheme as it was called when I wrote this.*

GOING HOME

Three more days of school
Three more days of sorrow
Three more days of this old dump
And we'll be home tomorrow.

Traditional

There's a Ladybird on Carol's Hair

There's a ladybird on Carol's hair
My chair leg's on my shoe,
I've yawned four times while teacher reads.
Do you think this story's true?
A giant with a beard of grass?
A castle made of soap?
I'd like to roll our vicar down
The Quarry's muddy slope.
I'm nearly seven,
I'm nearly seven,
I'm glad I've got a mole;
Yes, silly, in the garden shed,
I've covered it with coal;
My bottom's aching,
Can't we go?
Yes, up and chairs on desks
And all our hands together, so,
And keep us safe till morning light.
My cousin's got a lovely kite.
Ho, ho; ho, ho.
Yes Miss. Good night.

G. Harrison
(from 'Ploughing after School')

The Last Lesson of the Afternoon

I sit here in slumber, hitting my head
and chewing my pencil.
The teacher is groaning.
The clock ticks like a nightmare.
My cartridge is dry except for a few splotches.
The room is bare like a prison cell.
My back is aching and my fingers are like
an alien's with blue ink.
I gaze up and only see whiteness.
My desk wobbles.
I listen,
all I can hear is pens writing.
The teacher's desk is a mountain of books.
Then I am saved, the school bell rings!
There is a mad scramble to escape.
I get outside – and feel a breeze
gently go by me.

Justin Bailey (aged 9)

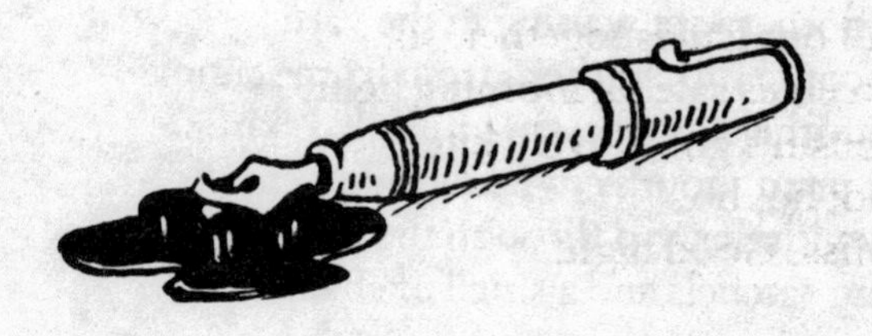

Evening Schoolboys

Hearken to that happy shout – the schoolhouse door
Is open thrown, and out the youngsters teem;
Some run to leapfrog on the rushy moor,
And others dabble in the shallow stream,
Catching young fish and turning pebbles o'er
For mussel clams. Look in that mellow gleam
Where the retiring sun that rests the while
Streams through the broken hedge. How happy
  seem
Those schoolboy friendships leaning o'er the stile,
Both reading in one book; anon a dream
Rich with new joys doth their young hearts beguile,
And the book's pocketed most hastily.
Ah, happy boys, well may ye turn and smile,
When joys are yours that never cost a sigh.

John Clare

For a Junior School Poetry Book

The mothers are waiting in the yard.
Here come the children, fresh from school.
The mothers are wearing rumpled skirts.
What prim mouths, what wrinkly cheeks.
The children swirl through the air to them,
trailing satchels and a smell of chalk.

The children are waiting in the yard.
The mothers come stumbling out of school.
The children stare primly at them,
lace their shoes, pat their heads.
The mothers swirl through the air to cars.
The children crossly drive them home.

The mothers are coming.
The children are waiting.
The mothers had eyes that see
boiled eggs, wool, dung and bed.
The children have eyes that saw
owl and mountain and little mole.

Christopher Middleton

Oh, Joyous House

When I walk home from school,
I see many houses,
Many houses down many streets.
They are warm, comfortable houses,
But other people's houses.
I pass without much notice.

Then as I walk farther, farther
I see a house, the house.
It springs up with a jerk
That speeds my pace; I lurch forward.
Longing makes me happy, I bubble inside.
It's my house.

Richard Janzen (aged 12)

Walking Home

There are
523 railings
29 steps
7 bus stops
14 trees
32 houses
1 antique shop
25 drains
And 1 roundabout
Between my house and school.

Tom Edwards

School's Over

School's over.

'Bye Lizz!'
'Bye Mandy!'
'Bye!'
Sun shouts
Like enormous tubas.
Women with tousled hair
Loll in doorways,
Too hot to chatter.
Their babies cry
And they do not care.

Home at last.
The house is lonely.
Dad's on the buses.
Mum works at the Co-op.
Lonely is cool.
Lonely is quiet.
I like it.
I read a bit
Then flick over the pages of the book
Impatient to get to the end.
No pictures.
I draw my own.
The heroine has brown hair and freckles.
The villain's a greasy grey.
Those caves under the hill
Where he hides the treasure?

An hour has passed.
Lonely is empty.
Is big, bare spaces
I'm afraid to cross.
No cat to purr
And rub against my legs.
Mum hates them.
Dad says they smell
Like geranium leaves.
I walk from room to room
Looking for my cat,
My dusty gold cat
With gooseberry eyes.
'Puss! Puss!' I say,
'Here's a bowl of cream for you.'
But he never comes.

Olive Dove

Index of titles

Acknowledgements

The author and publishers would like to thank the following people for giving permission to include in this anthology material which is their copyright. The publishers have made every effort to trace copyright holders. If we have inadvertently omitted to acknowledge anyone we should be most grateful if this could be brought to our attention for correction at the first opportunity.

Archie Barrett for 'My Picture'.
Bell & Hyman Publishers for 'Millicent and the Nature Ramble' by Doug Millband from *The Mishaps of Millicent Mary* .
Martin Brian & O'Keeffe Limited for 'The Magician' by Shaun Traynor from *Images of Winter* .
Cadbury Limited for 'Aristotle and Ballcocks' by Emma Payne, 'Go Away and Shut Up' by Colleen Boland, 'Thoughts' by Marcus Holburn and 'If the Teacher was a Robot' by Paul Marsh from *Cadbury's First Book of Childrens Poetry*; 'Art' by Olivia Frances Hum, 'This 'Ere School' by Stephanie Marshall, 'First Day at School' by Melanie Louise Skipper and 'Tashy the School's Rabbit' by Rachel Teggert from *Cadbury's Second Book of Childrens Poetry*; The Bully' by Paul Dingle, 'School' by Patrick McCoy, 'When I Was Lonely' by Teresa Steele, 'After Adrian Mitchell – We Liked His Stuff!' by Class 9, Tyldesly County Primary School from *Cadbury's Third Book of Children's Poetry;* and for 'I don't know' by Mhairi Boyle and 'Red Ink' by Sarah Rogers from Cadbury's 1986 Poetry Competition.

Jonathan Cape Limited on behalf of Roger McGough for 'He Who Owns the Whistle, Rules the World' from *In the Classroom*; on behalf of Adrian Mitchell for 'Dumb Insolence' from *The Apeman Cometh*.
Stanley Cook for 'The School', 'In the Playground' and 'Mr Fitzsimmons'.
Century Hutchinson for 'The Good, the Bored and the Ugly', and 'A Survey of Sovereigns' from *It's Funny When You Look At It* by Colin West; 'The Painful Way to Multiply', 'Words with Teacher' and 'Big Jim' from *Not To Be Taken Seriously* by Colin West; 'Back in the Playground Blues' by Adrian Mitchell from *I See a Voice* ed. Michael Joseph; and for 'Arithmetic' by Gavin Ewart from his *Collected Poems*.
Marchette Chute for 'Drinking Fountain' from *Around and About* published by Dutton, 1957.
Charles Davies for 'The Old School Bus', 'Martha Munch' and 'Winter Sports'.
André Deutsch for 'Riddle' by John Cunliffe from *Riddles & Rhymes & Rigmaroles*.
Peter Dixon for 'Oh Bring Back Higher Standards'.
Dobson Books Ltd for 'First Primrose' by Leonard Clark from *Good Company*.
Olive Dove for 'School's Over' and 'Write a Poem'.
Louise Draycott for 'Jolly Hockey Sticks!'.
Tom Edwards for 'James Bond Comes to Lunch', 'The Goldfish' and 'Walking Home'.
The English Centre, London for 'Us Dreads' by Dave Martin, 'I am a Deemmun' by Julia Ignatiou and 'A Close Shave' by David Bryant, all from *City Lines*.
Gomer Press for 'Thug' by Raymond Garlick from *Incense*.
Marian Gosling for 'Homework'.
Hamlyn Publishing Group for 'The Bionic Boy' by Charles Connell from *Versicles and Limericks*.
Harper & Row Limited for 'Six Times One' by Karla Kuskin from *Near the Window Tree*.
Harrap Limited and Little, Brown and Company for 'Lmntl' by David McCord from *Mr Bidery's Spidery Garden*.
Gregory Harrison for 'Distracted the Mother said to her Boy' from *A Fourth Poetry Book*, compiled by John Foster, first published by Oxford University Press, 1982.
Timothy Hattersley for 'Dinner Queue Dilemma'.
William Heinemann Limited and Doubleday for 'Miss Norma Jean Pugh, First Grade Teacher' by Mary O'Neill from *People I'd Like to Keep*.
David Higham Associates for 'The Fight' by Ted Walker, 'Conkers' by Clive Sansom, 'The Schoolboy' by Dylan Thomas and 'Summer Goes' by Russell Hoban.
Hodder & Stoughton Children's Books for 'First Day at School' and 'The Bully' by Rod Hull from *The Reluctant Pote*.
Julie Holder for 'The Loner'.
Paul Johnson for '1 x 1 is 2'.
Librairie Gallimard for 'How to Paint the Portrait of a Bird' by Jacques Prévert, translated by Paul Dehn, from *Paroles*.
Macdonald & Co. (Publishers) Limited for 'Lizzie' by Michael Rosen from *Wheel Around the World*.

Macmillan Publishing Company for 'The High School Band' by Reed Whittemore from *The Self-Made Man and Other Poems*, © Reed Whittemore 1959.
Wes Magee for 'Morning Break'.
Christopher Mann for 'I Don't want to go to School Today', and 'Johnson Broke My Ruler, Sir'. 'Government Health Warning', 'Science' and 'Keeping the Score'.
Michael Joseph for 'Bad Report' by Spike Milligan from *Unspun Socks From a Children's Laundry*.
Christopher Middleton for 'For a Junior School Poetry Book'.
Nerehurst Ltd for 'Red Cows' by Lydia Pender from *Poems for Fun*.
Leslie Norris for 'The Rebel Child' and 'Kevin Scores'.
Gareth Owen for 'A Stomach-ache is Worse Away from Home' and 'Friday Morning Last Two Lessons is Games Day'.
Penguin Books Limited for 'Hullo, Inside' by Max Fatchen from *Wry Rhymes for Troublesome Times*, Kestrel Books, © Max Fatchen 1983; 'Complaint', 'Lost' and 'The School Nurse' by Allan Ahlberg from *Please Mrs Butler*, Kestrel Books, © Allan Ahlberg 1983.
A.D. Peters & Co. Limited for 'The Leader' and 'Zebra Crossing' by Roger McGough from *Sky in the Pie*, Kestrel Books, 1983.
Punch for 'School Report' by Carole Paine.
Deborah Rogers Ltd for 'The Lesson' by Edward Lucie-Smith.
Michael Rosen for 'I was Mucking about in Class', first published in *A Third Poetry Book*, compiled by John Foster, Oxford University Press, 1982.
Vernon Scannell for 'Intelligence Test' from *The Apple Raid*.
Simon & Schuster, Inc. for 'The Wind' by James Snyder from *Miracles*, © Richard Lewis 1966; 'Oh, Joyous House' by Richard Janzen from *Miracles* © Richard Lewis 1966.
Stainer & Bell Limited for 'Impressions of a New Boy' by Marian Collihole from *Themework*.
Shirley Toulson for 'The Changeling'.
Mrs A. M. Walsh for 'The Blue Ball' from *The Roundabout by the Sea* by John Walsh (OUP).
Jane Whittle for 'Mr Mole', 'Teachers', 'The Last Exam', 'Thinking' and 'The Computer'.
Raymond Wilson for 'Playing Truant', first published in *A Fourth Poetry Book*, compiled by John Foster, Oxford University Press, 1982.